NATURAL OF ABERDEEN

'A Natural History of Aberdeen' tells the story of Aberdeen's wildlife past and present. It provides a fascinating account of the area's natural history from the earliest settlement to the present day and the book will be of great interest to anyone associated with the City and its surroundings.

Aberdeen has a surprisingly rich diversity of wildlife and this book, after describing the historical background and range of plants and animals in the City today, deals with some of the principal sites whose survival is a matter of controversy and raises the question of what value we put on the wildlife with which we live in such close contact in the city.

The author, Peter Marren, has written and lectured widely on the natural history of North East Scotland and since 1977 he has worked for the Nature Conservancy Council with special responsibility for Aberdeen, Deeside and Gordon Districts. Amongst Peter Marren's previous publications are monographs on the Muir of Dinnet and St. Cyrus National Nature Reserves and he contributes regularly to New Scientist, The Listener, Radio Scotland's Wildwatch programme, and Radio Aberdeen.

Peter Marren's experience of natural history and conservation, including degrees from Exeter and London Universities, together with his local knowledge and ability as a writer, combine to make this an informative and entertaining book for anyone interested in Aberdeen or natural history.

ISBN   0 907 184 03 0 (cloth).
       0 907 184 04 9 (limp).

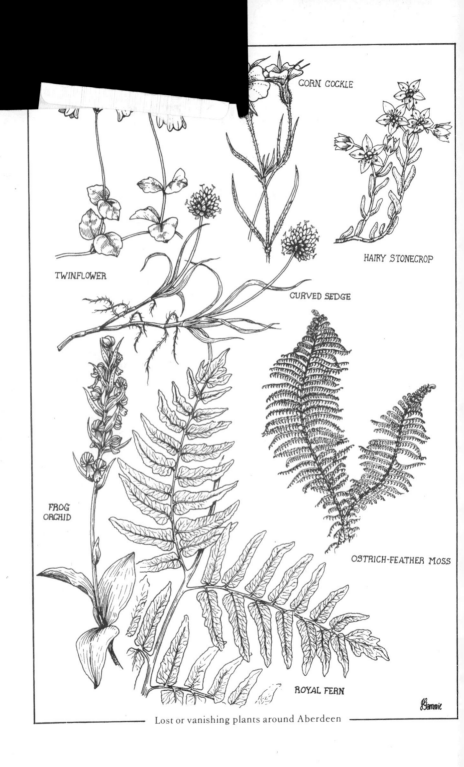

CORN COCKLE

HAIRY STONECROP

TWINFLOWER

CURVED SEDGE

FROG
ORCHID

OSTRICH-FEATHER MOSS

ROYAL FERN

Lost or vanishing plants around Aberdeen

A
NATURAL HISTORY
OF
ABERDEEN

By
Peter Marren

Published by
Robin Callander, Haughend, Finzean, Aberdeenshire.

1982

Printed by Aberdeen People's Press
163 King Street, Aberdeen

To Mark, Sandy and members of the
Aberdeen branch of the Scottish Wildlife Trust

Contents

List of Illustrations

Cover Illustration by Mike Taylor   Copyright.
Flower Plates pages 49, 50 and frontispiece by Jim Gammie   Copyright.

Preface and Acknowledgements

This book sets out to tell the story of Aberdeen's wildlife, past and present. Few of Britain's cities can compare with Aberdeen for the variety of places in which native plants and animals can find a home. The Granite City grew up around the estuaries of two important rivers, within sound of the breakers of the grey North Sea. The line of dunes fronting the shallow bay of Aberdeen gives way, south of the Dee, to a wild rocky coast, notched and serrated by narrow headlands and chasms. Above the shore rise undulating hills, the last gasp of the Grampians, whose heather and whin covered knolls conceal wet, peat-lined hollows and patches of scrubby woodland. It is a harsh landscape, and the approaches to Aberdeen remained wild and forbidding until comparatively recent times. Even today, it is possible to find places within walking distance of the city centre which one might associate more with national parks than with the precincts of Europe's premier oil town.

The neighbourhood of Aberdeen has a rich diversity of wildlife for so northerly a latitude with for example, over eight hundred recorded species of native and naturalised wild flowers and nearly two hundred and fifty species of birds, of which some eighty or so remain to breed. Nevertheless, with the wild riches and grandeur of upper Deeside and the Cairngorms not far away and readily available to most Aberdonians, some justification for a book specifically about the wildlife of the City of Aberdeen may be necessary. I would draw a distinction in kind between the wildlife of town and country. Places such as the Cairngorms are, for most of us, objects of brief and occasional visits. The City of Aberdeen, on the other hand, is where several hundred thousands of us spend most of our lives, and such wild animals and plants that it contains are our daily neighbours. The places in which these 'unofficial' inhabitants of the city find to grow, feed or nest are often man-made or intensively managed, and nearly always small in scale. Because of this, there is an unusual degree of intimacy between urban nature and the human community. In consequence, this book is really about two sub-jects: wildlife and people; within the context of the city, they are inseparable.

It is less easy now than in former times to define the limits of Aber-deen city. For convenience, I have used the boundary of the City Dis-trict, which was created in the local government reorganisation of the early seventies. The District includes not only the old parish of Aber-deen and the recent industrial development zones and dormitory suburbs, but also areas of open country which are still actively farmed. A fold-out map of Aberdeen City District will be found at the back of the book. The use of this boundary confers at least one important advantage in that all of the areas discussed in this book fall under the jurisdiction of a single local authority - and in matters affecting urban wildlife, it is usually the local authority which calls the tune.

There are few particularly rare species of wildlife occurring near Aberdeen, and most of the remaining patches of the indigenous veget-ation are very small, when compared with countryside further afield. Its value to the conservation of nature in Britain as a whole is not very great. The question which this book poses is more whether we wish to accomodate and encourage wildlife for values other than rarity, and the answer to this is largely dependent on the sort of surroundings we choose to live in. The policies and practices of Aberdeen City District Council often determine, by the management of open spaces under its control, what types of wild animals and plants occur in the City. In Aberdeen, as elsewhere, Council policies are designed for people and are very often detrimental to most forms of wildlife. It may be that some will consider that I have been over-critical of the Council on this score. I am writing from a particular viewpoint; the local authority has to take account of its responsibilities to the whole of the community, which inevitably places constraints on its actions. On the other hand, the imperatives of public safety and tidiness can, on occasions, lead to rather obsessive zeal, just as civic neglect can turn a flower-rich heath into a rubbish dump. The reader must decide whether my occasional strictures are justified, but I hope that none will regard them as an unsympathetic attack. Aberdeen is still a good place for a naturalist to make his home, and I, for one, have an abiding affection for its rugged countenance, warts and all.

This book would not have been possible without the help and advice of many people. I am particularly grateful to my employers, the Nature Conservancy Council, for their cooperation in the research and produc-tion of this book. I am also beholden to Robin Callander for his patience and many helpful suggestions, and to Maureen Beaton who prepared most of the typescript. To the following, who gave generously of their knowledge of Aberdeen and its wildlife, my grateful thanks: A.A. Cuthbert, Dr. M.B. Davidson, Professor C.H. Gimingham, P. Hope-Jones, J.A. Forster, Dr A. Knox, J. MacKay, E.M. Matthew, C. and H. Murray, Dr R. Owen, R.M. Palmer, Dr P. Racey, R. Rae, P. Sanders, M. Smith, Mrs A. Sommerville, J. Souter, Dr B.W. Staines, K. Watt, D. Welch, Professor V.C. Wynne-Edwards and Dr M.R. Young. None of them are, of course, responsible for any errors or misrepresentations in the text, and the opinions expressed, unless accredited separately, are mine alone.

Acknowledgement is due to the University of Aberdeen for permission to use material from unpublished theses and reports, and to the Department of Botany for permission to print the portraits of Professors Trail and Dickie. Likewise I am obliged to the Aberdeen University Bird Club for permission to quote from their Common Bird Census of Loirston Loch and to the North Eastern River Purification Board for permission to print the photomicrograph of *Sphaerotilus natans*.

It should be noted that this book describes private as well as public land, and although access to many of Aberdeen District's open spaces is unlimited, the owner's permission should be sought before visiting privately-owned properties.

PETER MARREN
Aboyne, October 1981.

I wondered why it is that we're all such bloody fools. Why don't people, instead of the idiocies they do spend their time on, just walk around *looking* at things. That pool for instance ... newts, watersnails, water-beetles, caddis-flies, leeches, and God knows how many other things that you can only see with a microscope. You could spend a lifetime watching them, ten lifetimes, and still you wouldn't have got to the end even of that one pool. And all the while the sort of feeling of wonder, the peculiar flame inside you. It's the only thing worth having, and we don't want it.

George Orwell,
Coming Up For Air

A single-minded man may by a right use of his eyes, anywhere that the sun shines, and the winds blow, and the rains fall, find abundant matter for observation and instruction.

William MacGillivray
A Natural History of Deeside and Braemar

Chapter 1

The Shaping of a City

No one knows how long people have chosen to dwell by the mouths of the Don and the Dee, nor at which point they first began to call their settlements by the collective name of 'Abirdene'. The early history of Aberdeen is lost in the mists of time, and when we first descry the faint outline of a town in that mist, in the early thirteenth century, Aberdeen already enjoyed the privileged status of a royal burgh. Some sort of habitation, perhaps little more than clusters of fishing huts, may have existed there for at least a thousand years before that. So far as we know, the Romans never came closer than the marching camp at Normandykes, near Peterculter, but a rough and wildly inaccurate map of Scotland, made by Ptolomy in the second century, indicates a north eastern coastal settlement named Devana on the north bank of a river, the Diva Fluvius, which some believe to be synonymous with Aberdeen and the river Dee. Nearly ten centuries later, a Norse saga refers to the town of 'Apardion', almost certainly Aberdeen, whose peace had been destroyed by the Vikings. It seems that by the eleventh and twelfth centuries, 'Apardion' had already built up a lucrative trading industry with Saxon and Fleming merchant fleets and was well worth the trouble of raiding.

The first definite date in Aberdeen's history is 1180, when King William the Lion granted a charter which guaranteed the burgh's existing trading rights. From the wording of the charter, we find that Aberdeen had been granted Royal Burgh status earlier that century in the reign of King David I (1124 - 1153), and still earlier Royal Charters may have been granted, although none, unfortunately, survive. Despite its favoured status, early Aberdeen must have been a small and lowly settlement, a cluster of wattle huts by the tidal flats of the Dee, in the vicinity of what is now Castlegate. It was a trading post in the wilderness. The growth of the infant burgh which led to the gradual reclamation of that wilderness is the subject of this chapter. Let us first take a look at how the area might have appeared before the people of Aberdeen began to modify their surroundings.

Like Rome, Aberdeen was built on seven hills. These were originally small pudding-basin shaped eminences with intervening wet, peaty hollows. Similar groups of small hills occurred nearby, and they formed a hummock-and-hollow landscape of the kind which can be seen today to the south of the Dee on Tullos Hill. These small hills were the product of deposition by melting ice, at the close of the last glaciation, when morainic sand and gravel were dumped in heaps by glacial streams, as the climate gradually grew warmer and the sheet ice retreated from the lowlands. A local geologist, Alexander Bremner, has compared the rise and fall of such close-packed 'herds' of hills with 'the ground-swell of an ocean, congealed after some prodigious storm'. Because of this small-scale unevenness, small bogs or 'marrishes' studded the surroundings of Aberdeen like bunkers in a golf course, and there were at least eight such bogs in the close vicinity of the burgh. One of them, which was later overlain by West North Street, has yielded the remains of willow, alder and birch trees from the peat bed. At least two larger hollows were permanently flooded: the Loch of Aberdeen, which lay to the north west of the early town, between it and the Denburn, and a smaller loch, the Loch of Old Aberdeen, a mile to the north. The peat-lands of Ferryhill were also partially flooded, and were probably little changed in the 1760s, when the area was described as 'little conical hills ... over-run with heath and furze, whilst the flat bottoms between them were drenched with stagnate water'.

The wet and boggy nature of the landscape was accentuated by the burgh's greatest asset, the great tidal basin of the river Dee. Until the nineteenth century, the Dee estuary was a wide expanse of tidal mud flats with broad mussel beds, saltings and shingle islands which were exposed at low tide. Reed beds and salt marsh formed where the Denburn and other streams passed into the estuary. The harbour basin was separated from the grey North Sea by the sandy, finger-like pro-montory of Futty.

In the Medieval period, the Don estuary was closer to the Dee than at present, and it is possible that little more than half a mile of dry land divided them. The Don estuary was narrower and more dynamic than that of the Dee, and it has changed its course over the centuries in accordance with natural changes in tidal erosion and deposition. At some stage, possibly as late as the sixteenth century, the earlier mouth of the Don was blocked by silt and blown sand, and the river channel swung northwards towards its present position. The old channel continued to flood, however, and the deepest part became a permanent loch known by Aberdonians as the Canny Sweet Pot. Between the rivers were open sand dunes, tufted with Marram Grass, through which clay hillocks like Broad Hill rose like sleepy whales. On the leeward side of the dunes there may have been low scrubland and heather, and the better pockets of soil hard by the town would have been among the first to be tilled.

To the west of Aberdeen, the land rises steadily to a plateau of three or four hundred feet, which is dissected by the valleys of numerous burns, of which the Denburn is the most prominent. Originally the slopes would have been covered by dense woodland, part of the great forest of Caledonia which stretched, with gaps for the highest mountains, from coast to coast. By the time Aberdeen received its first Royal Charter, an unknown proportion of the forest nearest the town would have been denuded by felling and fires, and converted to forest pasture or open heath. A sizeable area of near-natural woodland still remained however, notably the Royal Forest of Stocket, where kings retained the sole rights to timber and game. Since the forest was the earliest of Aberdeen's natural landscapes to disappear, let us have a closer look at what can be learned about it.

'THE GREEN GROWTH OF THE GREAT TREES'

It is possible to have a guess at the composition and wildlife of the vanished natural forests near Aberdeen, although solid evidence is lacking. On the best soils of the deeper river valleys, particularly the Don, oak would have been the commonest tree in a mixed deciduous forest of oak, ash, hazel and wych elm with smaller amounts of bird cherry, aspen, gean, alder and willows. The wild wood contained more dead standing timber than is usual today, and some of the mature trees would have reached a considerable age. One example was preserved into modern times, when an oak of enormous girth was dredged out of the Dee estuary in 1832[1] . As one progresses onto the more impoverished soils of the hillsides above the valleys, one would expect birch and Scots pine to replace oak as the dominant trees, and in the numerous boggy hollows we would find dense willow scrub. The forest in general would have been very variable, and any changes in its composition would probably have gradual rather than sudden.

The larger animals of Aberdeen's original forests would certainly have included many which are now extinct in Britain, although there is little documentary or archaeological evidence available about them. The Roman legions on their way through the area, might have seen bear, reindeer and the wild ox or auroch and boar, beaver and wolf survived well into the Medieval period. The skins and carcasses of wild forest game would have formed part of the staple trade with the Medie-

1   The much damaged remains were later transferred to Duthie Park, as a 'curiosity'.

val burgh, in exchange for salmon, cured fish and woven cloth. The forest game was evidently rich enough to attract royal hunting parties to the area, for most of the early Scottish kings shared a passion for the chase. Thus we have the story of the great wolf which is said to have attacked King Malcolm II in the Forest of Stocket in about 1010AD: That King's grandson, King Malcolm 'Canmore', suffered another dramatic encounter with the local wildlife in the form of a boar during a hunt in the nearby Forest of Cullerlie. The King, who in accordance with boar-hunting etiquette was on foot, would probably have been gored to death when a giant boar suddenly turned and attacked him, but for the presence of mind of one of his companions. Wrapping one arm in his plaid, this hunstman stuck it into the boar's mouth, and then proceeded to cut its throat with his dirk or 'sgian dubh'. The startled King, anxious to show his gratitude, thereupon gifted his companion with all the lands around within a hawk's flight which, we are told, became the barony of Skene, named after the sgian which slew the boar.

There were originally two Medieval forests close to Aberdeen: the Royal Forest of Stocket, which bent away to the north west, and Nigg Forest, which belonged to the Church and lay on the far side of the Dee. There are passing references to Stocket Forest in the burgh charters and records, but its appearance, the way it was managed, and its ultimate fate can only be guessed at by passing hints and clues. We first learn of its existence in 1313, when Robert Bruce granted custody of the forest to the burgh of Aberdeen and confirmed the grant with a charter in 1319. Bruce's famous charter which gave the burgh its 'Freedom Lands' in perpetual feu, is said to have reflected the King's gratitude for Aberdeen's loyalty during the wars of liberation. The Freedom Lands included all the *'fields, moors and other portions whatsoever of the said forest outwith the wood of Stocket, hard by the foresaid burgh of Aberdeen.'* But the King was careful to reserve certain royal prerogatives: *'we reserve for ourself and our heirs only, the green growth of the great trees in the foresaid wood and game likewise, should any such chance be found in the same forest.'* Like most Medieval kings, Bruce had a passion for hunting, and the royal right to 'vert and venison' was retained in nearly all of Scotland's royal forests. Bones found during excavations of Medieval sites in Aberdeen show that the venison was that of the Red Deer, which at that time was still a forest animal.

The wording of Bruce's charter suggests that the original woodland had already become fragmented, and that fields and moors now lay between the burgh and the forest, where once there would have been trees. Bruce had evidently reduced the boundaries of the royal forest within more manageable proportions but, even so, there were demands on the remaining timber. The trees were kept by two foresters, who were responsible to the Baillies of the burgh. Although they were supposed to be maintaining the forest in a fit state for kings to hunt in, there are hints in the burgh records that bribery and corruption ruled the day. The foresters were brought to trial for neglect of duty in 1398, 1400, 1410 and again in 1448, and there is reference to wood being cut illegally. Tenants living by the forest, and who had rights to cut timber for building, constantly exceeded their quotas, and in time the burgesses grew to regard the forest as their own property, to do with what they pleased.

The demand for timber of an expanding Medieval burgh was almost insatiable, in an age when nearly everything from ships and dwellings to tableware was made of wood. In a site at the Farquhar and Gill warehouse in the Medieval town, the acid, waterlogged nature of the ground has preserved intact the timber remains of thirteenth and fourteenth century domestic buildings. The timber can therefore be identified to show what use was made of the various local trees. The excavations showed that timber dwellings of that time were primitive to a degree: they consisted of birch posts sunk into a foundation trench, and interwoven with thin branches of wattle. Although some hazel was used as wattle, the local favourite was willow, whose thin, pliable shoots were ideal for the purpose. Supporting posts would prop up a roof which was evidently thatched with heather or bundles of rushes, and the post-and-wattle walls were smeared with mud or dung for added insulation. These houses suggest lives of grinding poverty and hardship, although it is possible that the excavated buildings were outhouses backing on to more substantial street houses of unknown construction. Such buildings required a phenomenal amount of timber: a miserable little hut of only nine square yards in area might require a thousand individual wattles. Moreover, such huts were unlikely to stand longer than twenty five to thirty years at most, and required constant repair, even when they escaped the fires which swept through the infant burgh from time to time (Aberdeen was burned to the ground [accidentally] in 1244 and again [deliberately] in 1335). A man might have to build three or more such timber dwellings in his lifetime, and fourteenth century Aberdeen had a population of at least 3,000.

The effect on the remaining woodland outwith the royal forest must have been enormous. Hilary Murray, who has reconstructed a model of the excavated Medieval buildings, suggested that the burgesses may have practiced a primitive form of coppicing in the willow beds, in order to provide a constant source of wattles. Otherwise, the woodland was probably converted to forest pasture, and the town's sheep, goats, horses, cattle and pigs would have made short work of any regenerating saplings. Thus the change from forest to moorland and pasture may have been rapid and irreversible.

As the local timber supplies dried up, the burgh seems to have closed in on what was left of the Royal Forest of Stocket. In 1494, a legal dispute over the ownership of the forest decided in favour of the burgh. This may have sealed its fate. At some stage between 1494 and 1606 the last remnants of the forest disappeared for ever. When, in the latter year, local oak timber was urgently needed to supply a new shipyard, the nearest available supply was the Wood of Drum, ten miles away. All that is left to remind us of the lost forest are placenames: Oakbank in Mid-Stocket, Foresterhill and Elrick, the latter being a term used for a drive of game which was often facilitated by wooden palisades. It is possible that the Elrick area marked the last stand of the great oaks of Stocket Forest. At some stage in the demise of the forest, the last wolves and boars also disappeared; indeed it is conceivable that the presence of wolves near valuable grazing land may have hastened the pace of forest clearance. What other kinds of forest wildlife perished with them, we can only speculate.

'THE COUNTREY IS BARRAN LYKE...'

Our earliest reliable maps of Aberdeen and its surroundings are those of Gordon of Straloch in 1656 and Parson Robert Gordon of Rothiemay in 1661. A glance at both maps shows that the landscape between the Don and the Dee had become almost totally denuded of tree by that time, to be replaced by barren moorland and bog, harsh and monotonous to the eye. The town itself was still very much on the Medieval pattern, centred around church and market place, but the population had probably trebled since the main series of burgh registers began in 1398.

The confusing division between the 'Old Town' and 'New Town' of Aberdeen probably dated from the burning of Aberdeen by English soldiers in 1335. It is unlikely that either of the two separate burghs is in reality much 'older' or 'newer' than the other, but by Parson Gordon's time, the two burghs had long been set in their respective roles: Old Aberdeen, with its magnificent Cathedral and College was an ecclesiastical burgh and the centre of learning; New Aberdeen, with its natural harbours in the Dee estuary, became the centre of trade and the service centre for north eastern agricultural produce.

Parson Gordon gave his own reasons for the growth of Aberdeen:

'Aberdeen exceeds not only the towns of the north of Scotland but likewise any city whatsoever of that same latitude for greatness,

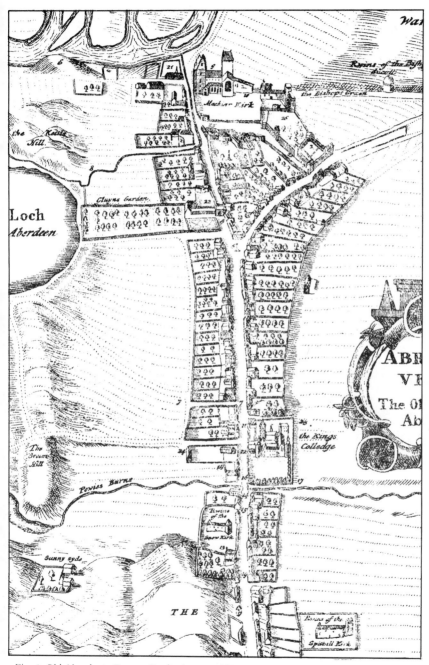

Fig. 1. Old Aberdeen, Parson Gordon's map 1661.

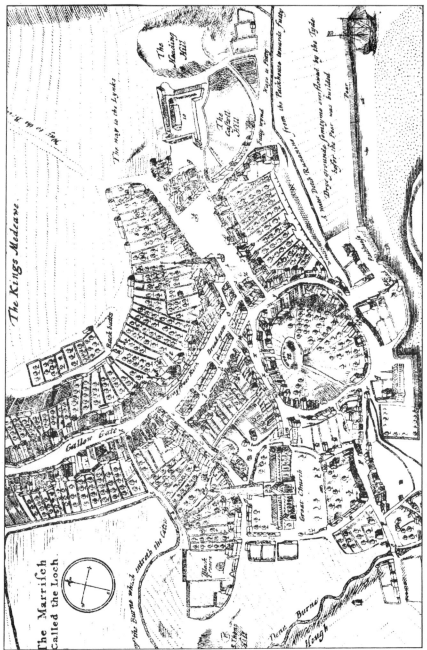

Fig. 2. New Aberdeen, Parson Gordon's Map 1661.

beauty and frequency of trading, The air is temperate and healthful about it and it may be that the citizens owe the acuteness of their wits thereunto, and their civil inclinations, the like not easy to be found under so northerly a climate, damped for the most part with air of a gross consistence...'

Between the mid-fourteenth century and Parson Gordon's time, many of the town's public buildings and some of its wealthiest private houses had been built of stone, but the average domestic dwelling was still made of timber. Most had long gardens opening directly onto crop fields, as Gordon's famous and oft-quoted description shows:

'Many houses have orchards and gardens adjoining; every garden has its postern and these are planted with all sorts of trees which the climate will suffer to grow, so that the whole town...looks as if it stood in a garden or little wood'.

We must be eternally grateful to Gordon for his valuable window on the past, but at the same time be conscious of his tendency to idealise mid-seventeenth century Aberdeen. Who would have thought from his description, for instance, that almost a third of the human population of this pretty and healthful town had perished through plague or massacre less than twenty years before? In the same way, his map of the town, although accurate in its general layout, was engraved by a Dutchman who had probably never set eyes on Aberdeen, and his matchbox houses and lollipop trees give an appearance of neatness and charm rather at variance with other contemporary descriptions. Nearer the bone was a reference in the burgh record to the problem of free-ranging pigs:

'in the churchyard they (the pigs) have cassin up great graves and incoverit dead corpses, which is both dangerous and shamefull, and they noways being waitit upone, doe converse in all filthie dunghills, middings, gutters and sinks of all sorts of excrements and by their working raise ane infectious and intollerable smell ... and also they may prove dangerous to young children and others quhen they are going at random through the streets'.

The pigs were not only smelly and dangerous: they were health problems. By an unfortunate coincidence of nature, man and pigs often share the same internal parasites, and among the excavated remains of Medieval cess-pits in Aberdeen are the preserved eggs of intestinal parasites such as the Nematode worm, *Ascaris*, which were probably transmitted to man by his close habitation with the pigs.

Except for within a mile or two of Aberdeen where the land was manured and cultivated intensively, the moorland surrounding the town defied attempts to improve it. Parson Gordon could find little to praise in the land a mile from the city gates:

> 'the countrey is barran lyke, the hills craigy, the plains full of marreshes and mosses, the fields are covered with heather or peeble stones, the corne feilds mixed with thes bot few'.

The roads to Aberdeen were appalling, even by the rough standards of the time, and travellers tales of pre-Improvement Scotland are full of accounts of its perils. One of the earliest is that of a Cromwellian soldier, Richard Franck, in his Northern Memoirs (1656):

> 'But what have we here? Cawses uncartable, and pavements unpracticable, pointed with rocky, stumpy stones and dawb'd all over with dingy dirt, that makes it unpassable; and the fields as I conceive, are ten times worse, because o'erspread with miry clay, and incumbered with bogs that will bury a horse.'

A century later another English traveller, George Colman, could still describe the approaches to Aberdeen in similar terms as 'a naked desolation, a waste of peat ... a barren, treeless moor.' Small, hopeless enclosures were set in the midst of heath, bog and huge masses of stone, unrelieved except for a few small, stunted plantations of fir. When Dr Johnson crossed the area in 1773, he compared it with the blasted heath of the three witches in Shakespeare's Macbeth. Boswell added, more prosaically, that 'it rained and the scenery was somewhat dreary'.

On the western border of the New town of Aberdeen was the Loch, a square-shaped hollow occupying a hundred acres or so, and replenished by the Westburn and Spital Burn. Attemps to culvert the inflow streams and drain the loch had been made as early as the fifteenth century, and by 1661, had partially succeeded. It is marked on Parson Gordon's map as a 'large fenny marrish, commonlie called the Loch, a fenne or pudle rather'. A drainage ditch circumvented the Loch, and was culverted by a system of dams and bulwarks. The basin must have continued to flood in winter and in wet years, but had otherwise become a peaty morass. Since it was a natural sink into which many of Aberdeen's gutters discharged themselves, it must have stank abominably in hot weather. The burgh records of 1633 say as much:

> 'The Loch was filthillie defyillit and corruptit, not onlie be gutteris daylie rynning in the burne, but also by listteris and the washing of clothes and abussing of the water in sindrie partis, with uther sorts of uncleanness.'.

This open sewer was used as the town's water supply and continued as such until the early eighteenth century.

Of the natural history of the Loch we know little. There is some evidence that it held marketable fish, presumably trout, and Aberdeen's great Civil War diarist, John Spalding, mentions its vast colony of 'maws' or gulls. It is probable that these were Black-headed Gulls, and their disappearance from the neighbourhood of Aberdeen can be dated with unusual accuracy:

> 'No maws were seen in the Lochs of New or Old Aberdeen since the beginning of the troubles and coming of soldiers to Aberdeen (in 1639), who were before flocked and clocked in so great abundance that it was pleasure to behold them flying above our heads, yea, and some made use of their eggs and birds'.

Spalding's regret at the departure of the gulls argues a tolerant, even affectionate (albeit utilitarian) regard for his avian neighbours. Two and a half centuries later, history repeated itself when another colony of hapless Black-heads were driven from Corby Loch, four miles to the north, this time by Victorian egg collectors.

Attempts must have been made from time to time to drain and grass over parts of the Loch, for in 1603, the Council were ordering that the wet reclaimed pasture be 'straitlie and diligentlie keipit' and 'yeirlie rowpit and putt to the grytest proffit and availl'. This was wishful thinking: the Loch defied early reclamation attempts, and the town's geese caused so much damage to the available grass in 1643, that they had to be removed.

G. and W. Paterson's map of Aberdeen in 1746[1] shows that the Loch had been reduced in size, but was marshy, with a small central pool. By this time, its usefulness as a water supply to the community had abated, since cleaner water was now available from draw-wells and the drinking fountain at Castlegate. In the 1730s, the Loch-lands were rented by Alexander Robertson of Glasgow, an enterprising early improver and a future Provost. Robertson set about draining and liming the marshy ground, and used the new-fangled farming methods of enclosure and crop rotation to take excellent successive crops of turnips, barley and rye-grass off it. Francis Douglas may have had this area at the back of his mind when he wrote, in 1782, 'it is perfectly astonishing to see the crops of grain and grass produced by ground which for so many ages had been neglected as unworthy of culture'.[2]

1 A survey of Old and New Aberdeen with ye adjacent country between ye Rivers Dee and Don. G & W Paterson.

2 Douglas (1782), General Description of the East Coast of Scotland from Edinburgh to Cullen.

But perhaps there was a more pressing reason than turnips and rye-grass for draining the Loch. Ague or malaria, transmitted by mosquitoes, was rife in the Scotland of the mid-eighteenth century, and George Sim (1903) suggested that it was this and not the advances of agriculture or the demand for building land, which first motivated the drainage of the Loch. Whatever the reason, the reclamation was remarkably thorough. In the late eighteenth century, when the expanding town finally broke through its earlier boundary, the site of the Aberdeen Loch finally disappeared under a ground-plan of new streets.

A stream about three feet wide, which continued to issue from the loch basin, was conveyed by covered channel to power a flourmill near St Nicholas Street in 1838, and, in 1865, was further diverted to the dam of Broadford works. Only in the name of Loch Street does any memory now survive of the 'marrish commonlie called the Loch'.

The Loch of Old Aberdeen was drained some time before 1782, for Francis Douglas describes its reclamation: 'on the north west of the town, contiguous to Gordon's Hospital, there is a bottom of rich land, where in former ages a loch or large pond of stagnant water stood. This loch was drained by the inhabitants; and the remains of it on the east are confined as a reservoir for driving some mills within the town'. Unlike its New Town counterpart, the basin of the Old Town loch is clearly visible on the ground (one crosses through it along St Machar Drive), and the bottom lands, which are now the playing fields of Powis Academy, still flood regularly in wet weather.

A SPIRIT FOR ENTERPRISE

The mercantile and market privileges, granted to the burgh of Aberdeen by the Medieval kings through a succession of royal charters were the mainstay of the economy of early Aberdeen. The earliest documentary evidence shows that Aberdeen then exported salmon, salt, fish, wool and hides, and that there was a domestic cloth making industry. The burgh was the main regional focus of the north east, and countryfolk would bring in panniers of wool and other local raw materials which were exchanged at the Castlegate market for fish and manufactured goods. Despite incessant civil strife, the burgh prospered.

Excavations at the Farquhar and Gill warehouse have shed some light on the early agricultural industry, although it is difficult to assess whether some of the finds represent home-grown products or imports. Seeds of flax plants found in the Medieval burgh middens indicate a linen industry, and the presence of Dyers Greenweed and Mignonette, both rare as naturally-occurring wild plants in the north east, suggests that they were grown or imported as a source of dyes for cloth. Figs and grape remains found on the site were presumably imports, the former being the main source of sugar at that time.

Little is known of the tillage of early Aberdeen, although it is reasonable to assume that the scattered crofts indicated on Parson Gordon's map between the Don and Dee and along the Denburn, had harbingers dating back to an early period. Much of the early agriculture was probably at a subsistence level. The Farquhar and Gill excavations have revealed plentiful grains of oats, wheat and the old-fashioned form of barley known as bere, together with the seeds of many weeds of arable land. Parson Gordon gives us our most detailed description of the pre-Improvement agricultural landscape and it is probable that the system of agriculture practised in his day had not changed in any significant way for centuries. Gordon's map shows that a belt of intensively cultivated land little more than a mile wide surrounded the town, with smaller crofting farmtowns further afield. This land was unenclosed, but divided into strips under the traditional 'run-rig' system, in which alternate ridges of the same field were tilled by the tenant with teams of oxen. Some of the boggy hollows, the coastal sand hills and the taller inland hills were left in their wild state. The soils of the cultivated belt were fed by 'fulzie', the manure of the streets and the burgh's midden heaps. The open fields of Futty supported a variety of crops ranging from wheat, bere and oats to root crops. Most of the land was under cereals at any one time, notably the 'Corne Feelds called somtyme The King's Medeawe', north east of the New Town, and the fields beyond the Denburn, from which Montrose's soldiers plucked sprigs of oats to stick in their hats before the Battle of Aberdeen, in 1644. A windmill stood on a small eminence at Gallowgate, close by the King's Meadow, and a mill had evidently stood here since 1271. Old Aberdeen was much the same, 'enclosed with little hills, pleasant corne fields, very fruitfull, and with pastures mixed amongst the ploughed fields'.

At the morass of Ferryhill, the feuars of the burgh had the right to cut peat - an essential for life in a landscape where timber had become scarce. They must have also utilised some of the wild plants of boggy ground, whose remains have been found within the town. Soft rush would have come in useful as thatching material, as well as heather, and the thickets of fragrant bog myrtle which covered the larger bogs, provided a multitude of uses: the basis for a spicy beer, a flea repellent used in bedding, a source of dye, and a ready-made supply of material for making besoms. On the drier braes, wild raspberry and blaeberry were gathered and eaten in season, and their seeds are among the most abundant plant remains found in the Medieval town.

The Act of Union in 1707 expanded Aberdeen's trade almost over-night, but for several more decades, the system of cultivation remained little changed, and arable land was confined to the best soils close by the town. The Patersons map of 1746 could still describe the land beyond Rubislaw, on the western marches of the town, as 'marshes and great stones, then chains of Mountains that stretch to ye Western Ocean.' Thirty years later, the wild moorland near Aberdeen had been largely reclaimed and put into productive use. An observer in the 1780s could state that 'as far as one can cast his eye round Aberdeen, there is not a vestige of the muir remaining'.

The agricultural revolution at Aberdeen, which was as sudden and dramatic as anywhere in Britain, was witnessed by an East Lothian farmer, Andrew Wight, who had been commissioned in 1778 to report on the state of husbandry in the north east. At that time, the system of agriculture employed in East Lothian was the most advanced in Scotland. As Wight travelled north on a series of surveys, he saw, by comparison, how miserable the standard of husbandry was in most counties other than his own. Kincardine fared particularly badly: 'I am sorry to observe that agriculture in this county makes little figure'. When he visited Aberdeen in the fall of 1779, Wight could, by contrast, scarcely contain his admiration:

> 'There is perhaps no place in the world where a spirit of husbandry has made such a figure as about Aberdeen. A corner between the rivers Dee and Don has for many years been cultivated in the most skilful manner by a mixture of the garden and field crops, one year cabbage, next year barley; one year turnip or oats, and so alternately, a mode of cropping unknown anywhere else in Scotland'. [1]

It seems that the new methods of agricultural improvement were a bandwagon, pioneered by a handful of forward thinking men like Alexander Robertson of Glasgow and Skene of Rubislaw, and jumped on by many others when they realised that new ways meant more money. The introduction, by Robertson, of clover, rye-grass and turnip, heralded the era of widespread improvement, although common land had been divided up and feued out at a rent since the end of the seventeenth century. Francis Douglas, writing in 1782, provides us with many vignettes of improvement in action:

> 'The lands of Ferryhill ... about twenty years ago, that the Community feued them out, were possessed by two tenants who exceed-

---

1   The Present State of Husbandry in Scotland. Reports to the Commissioners of Annexed Estates. Edinburgh, 1778.

ingly neglected them... The tenants, who rented them low, kept their best grounds in constant tillage, and never once thought of improving the more ordinary. When these farms were feued out, they fetched a great advance of rent, and fell into the hands of several proprietors'.

'We ascended an eminence called the Stocket-brae, the under part of which was feued out by the town about thirty years ago. Eighty two acres, thought unimprovable, were reserved to be planted with Scots firs, and accordingly were inclosed and planted, but have since been feued out and made arable'.

'Much of this ground (of Gilcomston) was feued out by Mr Skene of Rubislaw and, though never before worth 6d per acre, now yields his heir between fifteen and twenty shillings, some of it more ....'

'... a tract of improved ground (Loanhead) formerly the town's common pasture, which, since the beginning of this century, has been feued out by the community, at a small quit rent per acre'.

Although the reclamation of the wilderness demanded every resource of patience, perseverence and capital from the improver, some problems were not as hopeless as they looked. To clear a field of stones, for instance, might cost the formidable sum of £30, but the canny land-owners soon realised that they could recover most of this by selling the stone to builders. By such means, most of the land near Aberdeen was brought into productive use within a generation.

In the meantime, men had begun to harness some of the local resources of material and energy for their own needs. It is probable that the river Dee had long been used for transporting logs from the dwindling and ever remoter forests to Aberdeen. By 1661, Aberdeen was already a town of water mills: Gordon Mills and Keithaks Mill on opposite banks of the Don, Gilcomston Mill by the burn of that name and Justice Mills on the How Burn. In the eighteenth century, the waters of the Don and Dee would power one of Aberdeen's key industries, its paper mills - and an attempt was made to found a paper mill at Gordon Mills as early as 1696. Less successful was a remarkable early atttempt, in 1616, to harness wave energy to power a pair of corn mills.

Aberdeen had no resources of coal or minerals, which precluded the growth of heavy industry. What it did have in abundance was rock. The earliest stone buildings in Aberdeen were made of irregular blocks of sandstone, most of which were gathered from local fields. After a serious fire in 1729, it became the custom to replace straw or heather thatch with roof slates, and to face all new buildings with stone. From this time onwards, Aberdeen's hard grey granite was used as building stone in increasing quantity, and by the early nineteenth century was one of the town's main exports. The earliest known granite quarry dates from 1604, and was used to supply stone for window sills and lintels. Two more were established in the early eighteenth century. Most of the pre-nineteenth century granite was obtained from Nigg and Torry, where it could be chipped away from the coastal cliffs without the need for deep excavations. Demand began to outstrip supply towards the end of the eighteenth century, when Aberdeen granite was being exported for London's paving stones. An inland quarry was established on the rich seam of granite at Rubislaw, but until the invention of the steam derrick and cableways in the 1870s, such quarries were limited to comparatively shallow scoops in the grounds. The industry really took off in the last quarter of the nineteenth century.

Without a good harbour Aberdeen's industrial enterprises would have been still-born. The story of the reclamation of the Dee estuary, beginning with the removal of the great rock of Craig Metellan by 'Davy do A'thing' in 1610, has been told so often that only the barest outline will be given here. By Parson Gordon's time, a sizeable area of estuarine saltings had been reclaimed by the construction of a stone pier, which provided a promenade between the harbour and town. No doubt Aberdeen benefitted in this respect from the advice and expertise of its trading partners, the Dutch. Breakwaters had also been built at the river mouth between 1607 and 1610. Inlet burns were diverted into new channels, the Denburn in 1648, and the Trinity Burn in 1767, when Virginia Street was built over the latter's old course. The transformation of the natural estuary, with its treacherous Inches and saltings, 'whereof most pairt is usually overflowed by the Tyde', awaited the fishing boom of the nineteenth century. The first docks of the late eighteenth century were followed by the building of the walls of Waterloo Quay between 1811 and 1834, and the widening of the channel to create Victoria Dock in 1848. In 1869 the mighty Dee itself was diverted to a new channel, thus bringing the taming of the estuary to a triumphant conclusion.

In following the development of the port, we have strayed into the granite years of Aberdeen's greatness. Well before the finishing touches had been made to the dockyards, the appearance of Parson Gordon's Aberdeen had changed beyond recognition. Walking the streets of Aberdeen today, one only occasionally passes buildings which Parson Gordon and his forebears would have known: apart from the major collegiate and religious buildings, there is Provost Ross's house in Shiprow, and Provost Skene's house in Gallowgate, shrinking beneath the plate glass ramparts of St Nicholas House, surely one of the world's most remarkable architectural confrontations. The Aberdeen of old bears little resemblence to the modern city. Although Aberdeen's surroundings were transformed in the agricultural revolution, the transformation of the city itself had to wait another thirty years for the second revolution - that of granite.

Chapter 2

The Granite Age

At the beginning of the nineteenth century, Aberdeen was a small compact town with thirty narrow streets and a population of twenty seven thousand. At its close, the population had risen to one hundred and fifty three thousand and the streets numbered five hundred. The century saw the passage of a Medieval burgh, centred on church, castle and market-place into a modern regional focus. One can point to a single moment in history when Aberdeen suddenly sloughed the Medieval skin it had worn for centuries. This was the laying of the foundation-stone of Union Bridge by Provost Dingwall on 7 July 1801, the step which was to take Union Street across the Denburn, and lead to the great westward expansion of the city. The new straight and level thoroughfares of Union Street and George Street, followed by Thomas Telford's Don Bridge and King Street in 1830, laid the ground plan of a new network of streets as regular as a crossword puzzle, and completely different from the undulating wynds of the Medieval burgh.

The building blocks of the new Aberdeen was granite of uniform hue: North Sea grey with a flash of mica. Architects such as Archibald Simpson (1790 - 1847) were soon producing virtuoso displays of the possibilities of this granite as building stone. Union Street, Albyn Place and Golden Square were modelled along classical lines, whose buildings were as simple and severe as the stone that made them, but possessed withal, elegance and solidity. The later baronial and Gothic styles went to the other extreme. I think there are no more enjoyable buildings in Aberdeen than those baronial suburban houses which prosperous merchants used to demand, with their parapets, weathercocks, fish-scale roof slates and conical turrets, visible signs that all was well with the occupier's bank balance.

The granite industry is said to have 'brought gold to Aberdeen'. If so, the gold-rush was initiated by the invention, in 1810, of machinery to polish and dress granite blocks, which soon resulted in a production line of sixty polishing yards and a thriving export trade. New techniques later enabled the most lucrative seam of Aberdeen's distinctive grey and white granite at Rubislaw Quarry to be fully exploited, and this vast hole seemed inexhaustible. To the Aberdonian in Victorian times, it would have seemed inconceivable that any other building stone would ever be used.

The expanding population of Aberdeen	
1396	c.3,000
1661	c.9,000
1755	15,730
1801	27,608
1821	44,600
1900	153,000
1948	188,800
1971	254,785
1980	307,177
1991 (predicted)	325,277

With the crossing of the Denburn, the town grew steadily outwards from its old Medieval core like the concentric rings of an onion. Futty, for long a separate parish with its own church, was absorbed by port development and given the more genteel name of Footdee. The building of the Victoria Bridge across the Dee in 1881, stimulated the growth of Aberdeen's first satellite suburb of Torry, rows of tenement and terraced housing designed for the new industrial working classes. Another way across the Denburn was forged at Rosemount Viaduct. Spacious suburban villas spread over former open fields and heaths in the neighbourhood of Rubislaw and Mid-Stocket, whilst in the less favoured areas, the workers were packed into less airy quarters, close by their dark satanic mills.

The creation of the granite city had many important consequences for the nature of the wildlife of Aberdeen parish. Rural habitats were gradually replaced by specifically urban ones: town parks, waste grounds, railway lines, gardens. The more natural areas were often reclaimed by using the greatly increased quantity of domestic rubbish to lay the foundations for new development. These changes form the subject of this chapter.

The boom years of urban expansion in the last third of the nineteenth century, saw the elimination of most of the wild corners of the old Parish of Aberdeen. It was not just the direct effects of new housing which wrought the change, but also the transformation in the city's outlook from a remote rural town into a bustling modern city. Until 1870, Aberdeen contained two tidal estuaries, a mile and a half of natural sand hills, a botanically-rich heath and innumerable smaller havens for wildlife, such as turf walls, mill ponds and old quarries. Most of these were swept away within little more than a generation.

We can illustrate the nature of this change by concentrating on two relatively wild areas which were regularly visited by the University botany classes, led, during almost the whole of this period, by Professor James Trail. One of these excursions was along the banks of the Dee. Although the Dee estuary had been considerably modified since Parson Gordon's time, by the creation of docks, artificially deepened harbours and quays, the greater part of its banks were in a comparatively natural condition until 1869. They were naked of trees, except for a few stunted alders and willows, but the rough banks, river shingle and small patches of saltings were full of a variety of wild flowers. In the brackish water by the suspension bridge was one of only two places in the north east where the Tassel Pondweed could be found, whilst on the shingles and open river banks, a colourful array of wild flowers, including Globeflowers, Northern Bedstraw and Water Plantain grew, and there was always a chance of finding other mountain plants, brought down by the river from further upstream (see page 72). The turf banks of Allenvale Cemetery, above the river, was the place to see Shepherds Cress, whilst a recess in a wall at Ferryhill was where one paid ones respects to the Bur Chervil. In 1869, work began on the cutting of a new channel for the Dee below the suspension bridge, an operation which was completed three years later. The old river course was filled in with refuse and levelled, later to be covered by railway marshalling yards and flour mills. The new channel of the Dee was virtually a canal with artificial banks, and the plants of the muddy shores of the old estuary died out completely. Further upstream, a carriageway and esplanade were simultaneously built along the north bank of the river as far as the Brig o' Dee, and the old shore banked up with stones. Only upstream of the Brig o' Dee was the bank left in a comparatively natural condition, and this continued to be a regular haunt for botanical excursions until the walkway was closed to the public in 1880.

A second popular route for botanical excursions was to take the country road from Rubislaw Terrace to Rubislaw Den and then follow a track to some old granite quarries. These, according to Trail, were 'then covered part in trees, and in part were almost treeless, with pools in some places and in others mounds of rubbish, bare on some slopes, while on other parts they were covered with tangled vegetation... (they) always gave a rich harvest'. The quarries then lay in an area of country lanes, with earthen walls and plenty of wild corners. The wildest of all was Stocket Moor, which lay between the Skene Road and the Denburn, a fine sweep of natural heathland with boggy hollows and small burns. This was where botanists would converge to see the animals and plants 'distinctive of heaths and of marshy moor'. The whole of this area was transformed into middle-class suburbs of solid granite between 1880 and 1900. Stocket Moor was first broken up and cultivated, and finally disappeared under houses. Waysides, earth walls and hedges were replaced by paving stones, and most of the quarries were filled in and levelled. Indeed, it was not long before Professor Trail found it 'difficult to trace in that corner the haunts of former botanical rambles'. Rubislaw Den survived, but access to it became more restricted and difficult, and visits by the botanical classes gradually ceased.

By 1920, Trail was to gloomily assert that 'there are not now any such botanical excursions within the Parish (of Aberdeen) as then existed (in 1869)'. Perhaps he was being a little too pessimistic; the Don valley was still in a comparatively natural condition, and the Parish of Nigg, to the south of the Dee, was almost entirely rural. But the heart of the Aberdeen we know today was largely fashioned in the critical period between 1869 and 1910. The changes to Professor Trail's third excursion area were the most dramatic of all and to naturalists at the time, the most distressing: The reclamation of the Links.

QUANTITIES OF SAND

The late nineteenth century local authority's attitude towards Aberdeen's natural sandhills could be compared with that of Lewis Carroll's Walrus and Carpenter:

> They wept like anything to see
> Such quantities of sand:
> 'If this were only cleared away,'
> They said, 'it would be grand!'

For most of Aberdeen's history, the line of sandhills between the Don and the Dee remained in a comparatively natural condition. Parson Gordon's map of Aberdeen shows that the gently undulating natural grassland of the Links was fronted by a narrow ridge of sand and backed by a network of run-rig agricultural fields which separated the sand-hills from the burgh. Roughly half way along the dunes, the level ground was interrupted by a series of small hillocks. The most seaward of these was the Broad Hill, and between this and the Gallow Hills to the west ran the road from Castlegate to the Bridge of Don.

North of the Broad Hill, the Dunes widened and their outline became more ragged. In their midst was a shallow, elongated loch known as the Canny Sweet Pot, which drained northwards into the Powis or Tile Burn. According to Parson Gordon, the Pot measured seven hundred and sixty walking paces long, and from fifty to a hundred paces wide. Gordon also recorded a tradition, repeated on later maps, that,

'The River of Done is said credibly to have run through the Loch of Canny Sweet Pott of Old and thence to have turned its streame eastward entering ye sea under the Broad hill.'

Although the Don occupied a similar channel in 1661 to the present-day one, a rather ambiguous record in the burgh archives suggests that its course wound a mile to the south at least as late as 1521, before this channel became blocked by sand. Storm waves frequently broke through a wide break in the dune ridge near the Canny Sweet Pot and its water must have been at least partially saline. Between the Tile Burn and the Don was low-lying grassland which was prone to flooding at high tide, and formed a wide flat of grazed salt marsh. The Don estuary itself had wide tidal mud flats and shifting sand spits, teeming with wild birds, and might have been very similar in appearance to the present day estuary of the North Esk.

There are few references to the wildlife of the Links before 1800, but two sets of chance records are of special interest. The first of these concerns the mysterious arrivals and departures of the Aberdeen cony or rabbit. The rabbit is reported from the Links of Aberdeen in Exchequer Rolls of the fourteenth and fifteenth century and it had probably been introduced there for its valuable fur and flesh. The nearby place-name 'Cunnigar Hills' probably refers to those early rabbits ('cunnigare' is Old Scots for a rabbit warren). The Burgh minutes of 1503 and 1511 state that the rabbit then flourished on the Links south of Donmouth, and these records confirm that it had been established there deliberately. Three centuries later, the rabbits seem to have gone. They receive no mention in the Old Statistical Account and in 1811 it is said that there were 'not a hundred in the whole county'. According to the New Statistical Account (1843), the rabbit was reintroduced to the north east in the 1830s, since when, of course, it multiplied with alarming rapidity and soon became a pest. The agricultural revolution probably aided its spread, and its original north eastern home seems to have been on the coastal sand hills of Aberdeen.

The second early reference relates to the duneland vegetation. The burgh minutes of 1715 refer to 'the Carpet Walk' across the dunes, so named because of the 'softness and thickness of the wreathed green moss with which it is overspread'. Recent archaeological excavations have suggested that this soft, thick moss had at least one important use, in the days when paper was still expensive. Plants remains from what are thought to have been Medieval cess-pits include large amounts of moss, which had presumably been gathered locally. Within the moss fragments were found the remains of human intestinal parasites. The conclusion seems inescapable - the moss was a precursor of lavatory paper! The archaeologists have even enabled this 'wreathed green moss' to be identified: it is an attractive, feathery species with a red stem, called *Hylocomium splendens.*

By 1870, the Links north of Broad Hill retained their natural character although the coastline was considerably more disturbed than a century before. To the south, the old point-to-point along the sands had been replaced by a more formal circular race course on the Queens Links in 1790, and factories occupied the old Links of Futty and its agricultural fields. The Canny Sweet Pot had been reduced in size, and divided into two separate small pools, through which a small stream fed north into the Tile Burn. More significant perhaps, were the effects of improvements to the Don estuary. In 1727, the Donmouth had been artificially banked with a bulwark of stakes and stones, in order to prevent the river flooding regularly into the Links along its old channel. These defences were improved and extended in 1822-24, and the result must have been to alter the character of the grazing marsh, converting it into high grade pasture with the loss of many of its salt-marsh plants. The Kings Links and the dune ridge were still intact, however, although in their midst was a brickworks which dated back to the 1830s.

Judging from the floras of Dickie and Trail and their predecessors, the Kings Links were once rich in coastal plant life and they held a full range of plants of sandhill and estuarine habitats. Just above the high tide mark grew the strand-line plants, such as Sea Rocket, Saltwort and Babington's Orache. Behind the low embryo dunes was the open 'yellow dune' ridge, with its thick tussocks of Marram Grass and a diversity of dune plants; behind that was the stabilised sand dune pasture, the saltings and the margins of the loch and burns. Almost all of the commoner wild flowers of the north east sandy coast occurred here somewhere, and many of the rarer ones in addition: a site which would rank with the very best available today.

Towards the end of the nineteenth century, a series of events took place which drastically altered the character of the Links, and virtually obliterated their native flora and fauna. The arrival of the railway transformed Aberdeen 's communications with the outside world. No longer was the city a remote northern burgh, but a place within the reach of anyone who wished to have a week-end's golfing and fishing, or indulge in the newly fashionable craze for seaside pastimes. Train loads of tourists provided a valuable new resource for the city's economy, and the Council set about increasing the attractions of Aberdeen's main attribute: its two miles of sandy coastline. The climax to a quarter century's steadily increasing use was the building of the esplanade and carriageway between Queens Links and Donmouth. The natural irregularities in the dunes were ironed out. The authorities soon discovered that they could kill two birds with one stone by using the hollows in the dunes to solve their increasing difficulties with refuse disposal, and then using the tips as a foundation for fashioning the land anew.

Thus the city's refuse became the foundation for the new improved Links. Much of the low-lying pasture between the Broad Hill and East Seaton was covered by a liberal helping of domestic rubbish, and turned into a recreation ground by the addition of a few inches of topsoil and a sowing of lawn grass. A football pitch was created on top of a heap of cinders below Broad Hill; football had been practised on the Links for centuries, and it was the land not the land-use which had changed. Much the same could be said about the golf course on Kings Links. This at least escaped the refuse and cinders, but the surface was levelled for fairways and greens, and the heather and whins were grubbed up, except where they were left as 'rough'. Some of the natural grassland was fertilised and resown with 'fine grass' mixtures whilst, ironically, some of the natural fine grass was dug up and removed for gardens and shooting butts.

In the meantime all was far from well with the Canny Sweet Pot and its burns. For some time, Tile Burn had been used as an open sewer, serving parts of Old Aberdeen and Woodside and, by around 1910, it finally disappeared from view altogether, to the loss of the wading birds which had formerly congregated by its banks. The Canny Sweet Pot suffered an even more undignified fate. Trail records that it had been 'reduced to two filthy quagmires, through which flowed a small stream, laden with the overflow from a sewage farm (and finally) disappeared under town refuse, the stream having been turned into a subterranean drain.'

In 1907, the City purchased Seaton Links, the last remaining part of the original dune vegetation, in order to extend the carriage drive, now used by noisy horseless carriages, westwards to the Bridge of Don, thus completing the circuit of the esplanade. The road embankment, and the reclamation of the nearby sandy and marshy ground which followed, spelt the coup de grâce for the natural coastline vegetation south of the Don. By 1923, only isolated pockets remained.

Of the more sensitive wild flowers of the Aberdeen Links, Trail witnessed the loss of Purple Milkvetch, Meadow Saxifrage, Frog Orchid Red Blysmus, Curved Sedge, and Water Whorl-grass, as well as the reduction of formerly widespread plants to one or two small and vulnerable places. In many cases, the road to extinction, whether slow decline or sudden catastrophe, can be traced by comparing successive local floras. Here are five examples of wild flowers which found the dramatic transformation of Aberdeen's sandy shores more than they could put up with.

1) The Oysterplant, *Mertensia maritima*
   'In the sand at Donmouth but in extremely small quantity' - Northern Flora, 1835. Presumed extinct through natural causes shortly afterwards.

   'Abundant in Nigg Bay,'

   -Dickie, 1860.

   'used to be not uncommon among the shingle of the Bay of Nigg; but the removal of the shingle to form concrete blocks used in building the South Breakwater at the mouth of the Dee, led to the extirpation from Nigg before 1880'.

   -Trail 1923.

Nearest known locality in 1980: Aberdour Bay, Buchan. The Oysterplant has declined nationally in recent years, probably for natural climatic reasons.

2) Curved Sedge, *Carex maritima*
   'Old Town Links, banks of ye rivulet going to ye low loch. Again in immense quantity on the flat (upper end) which lies along the (sand)-hills, creeping among sand which seems to have encroached upon the links.'

   -James Beattie, c 1800.

   'Old Town Links by the side of a road through the sand hills, a little north from the Broadhill'.

   - Dickie, 1860.

   'One or two plants still survived in (the above) place until 1870; but changes in the Links appear to have led to its extinction. A few plants grew on the north shore of the estuary of the Don, near the Coastguard Station; but I have not seen any there since 1880.'

   - Trail, 1923.

Nearest known locality in 1980: Sands of Forvie Nature Reserve.

3) Water Whorl-grass, *Catabrosa aquatica*
   'In a ditch at the west end of Old Aberdeen Links, south from the
   brick-work'.

- Dickie, 1860.

'For a number of years it seemed to have disappeared from the
Links; but in 1885 it grew in profusion in and around the upper
pool of Canny Sweet Pot and into the ditch flowing into the pool.
For some years it appeared to thrive there, though much eaten by
cattle. The pool and ditch have (since) been filled up, and with
them the grass has disappeared.'

- Trail, 1923.

Nearest known locality in 1980: Blackdog Links, where it may have been
extirpated by tipping in 1979. This beautiful grass is almost extinct in
the north east, a victim of field drainage.

4) Baltic Rush, *Juncus balticus*
   'Marsh upon the coast, north of Donmouth'

- Cow, c 1836.

'Formerly in a small marsh near the sea on the Links north of the
Don, about a mile from Donmouth. The rush had disappeared
before 1870, when I first looked for it there: and the marsh has been
drained since the Balgownie golf course was formed.

- Trail, 1923.

Nearest known locality in 1980: Loch of Strathbeg nature reserve.

5) Frog Orchid, *Coeloglossum viride*
   'Generally common around Aberdeen'.

- Macgillivray, c 1850.

'I have found a very few examples, the last in 1902, on short turf
on the inner sand-dunes of the Links, near the mouth of the Don.
Still plentiful on Balgownie Links'.

- Trail, 1923.

Nearest known locality in 1980: Foveran Links.

Despite the gradual ruin of Aberdeen's duneland flora and its
associated fauna between 1870 and 1920, one dune plant actually
increased during that period. This was the Lyme Grass. The earliest
known record is from Donmouth in 1802, and Trail, who documented the
subsequent spread of the plant, suggested that it had been unintention-
ally introduced into the area by fishing boats. For seventy years, Lyme
Grass remained local and uncommon, but from 1870 onwards, it underwent a population explosion, spreading in a narrow belt along the

broken dunes of the foreshore, and further inland along river channels and 'blow-outs' in the dunes. This sudden increase may have been connected with disturbance to the dunes, although the grass also went on to colonise the relatively undisturbed dunes further north. Its spread had one undesirable side-effect: this coarse, aggressive tall grass crowded out all competitors on the foredunes, and smaller annual plants such as Sea Rocket became less widespread in consequence. Lyme Grass is still abundant in the remaining fragments of open dune, such as the sand spit at Donmouth.

The rape of the Links also saw more ephemeral changes to the vegetation. Trail assiduously catalogued the many plants that colonised the refuse tips, which soon flaunted their own exotic flora of pioneer plants and casual weeds, so different from that of the dune grassland buried beneath. Some species, hitherto very rare in the Aberdeen district, such as Lesser Bindweed and Woody Nightshade, sprouted in abundance from their odious surroundings, until they were buried in their turn by tarmacadam and topsoil.

CANALS, DOCKS AND THE RAILWAY

The emergence of Aberdeen into a leading trading and manufacturing town was made possible by the vast improvement in communications in the nineteenth century. The old cattle tracks and pack horse trails, which had been cursed and reviled for centuries, were replaced by McAdam's modern roads and turnpikes, whilst the capacity of the harbour was steadily improved during the long years of the fishing boom. The revolution in transportation gave Aberdeen two habitats which both, in their different ways, were to become wildlife reservoirs, harbingers of a truly urban flora and fauna adapted to man-made constructions. These were the canal and the railway.

The Don valley canal, which linked Aberdeen to Port Elphinstone, near Inverurie, had a life of less than fifty years. It was designed by that master of civil engineering, Thomas Telford, and built between 1796 and 1807, with the primary aim of stimulating local farming enterprise and facilitating the transport of agricultural produce. We know a little about its plant life, since the Aberdonian stretch of the canal is mentioned in the early local floras of the 1830s. It's waters were drawn from the Don, and many of the characteristic aquatic plants of that river were therefore able to colonise its banks and silty bed. Among these were Flag Iris, Flote Grass, Water Milfoil and at least six species of pondweed. The canal resembled, in fact, a slow, deep lowland river, which wound into the very heart of the city, and must have provided many freshwater plants and animals with a congenial habitat, in place of Aberdeen's lost natural lochs. The Canadian Pondweed, which rapidly choked much of Britain's canal network after its introduction in 1842, was never found in the Aberdeen canal, perhaps because it was also absent from the river Don.

In Aberdeen, as elsewhere, the coming of the railway killed the canal trade. In 1853, the Great North of Scotland Railway Company bought up the canal company and set about draining the canal, with the intention of using its water-course for the Inverness railway line. Indeed, so rapidly did they drain it that canal barges were left stranded on the mud and the channel had to be filled again to remove them. This was the age of railway mania. A railway viaduct had already spanned the Dee and a terminus been built on the former moss of Ferryhill, although it was transferred in 1854 to the present site at Guild Street. The year before, the Deeside line to Banchory had been opened. The main effect of the railway era on Aberdeen's natural history was an explosion in the flora of 'alien' plants. The laying of ballast, usually well-mixed with refuse of all types, brought in a host of weeds, some of which are relatively rare except in ports and industrial areas.

A very detailed record of the weeds and aliens of Aberdeen was kept by Professor Trail, between 1869 and 1920. One particular piece of ground fascinated him. This was the old channel of the Dee, which had been cut off and drained during dockyard improvements in 1872, and infilled with 'town refuse of a very mixed sort'. Part of this land between the Guild Street station and Market Street was enclosed by a fence to keep out intruders. Trail was allowed access to this ground in 1893 by the (probably slightly bemused) railway authorities, and in the following years he made a careful census of every species he could find. 'On this ground', he wrote, 'grew up a strange medley of native plants and of aliens, which for a few years were left almost undisturbed to settle the struggle for existence as they might'. He certainly uncovered a richly exotic hoard. 'Multitudes' of orange trees, grapevines, tomatoes and date palms, doubtless the sweepings of some fruiterer's shop, sprang up from the levelled surface of the rubble. Exotic seeds, perhaps dumped by a cage bird merchant, produced canary grass, maize and tares, as well as groves of cannabis (which was sometimes accompanied, suitably enough by the Opium Poppy). Foreign grain, used in the adjacent flour mill, produced another fertile haul of 'casuals' - alien plants which are unable to establish themselves for long. Many of these came from Konigsberg in East Prussia, where the seed grain was usually less 'clean' than the homegrown product, and among the Prussian casuals, the legumes are particularly well-presented. The proximity of the site to the dockyards aided the spread of casuals from still further afield. Some, the so-called 'wool aliens', were brought in as seeds entangled in imported wool. Another source of incomers were the bales of esparto grass, which were imported for paper making. According to George Sim (1903), 'various species of lizards' escaped from among the esparto grass in the neighbourhood of the harbour and Waterton papermill, although unfortunately he does not tell us what kinds of lizards they were.

Trail recorded a total of four hundred and seventy species of alien plants from Aberdeen, many of them from the railway ballast and refuse of the Market Street area, and that is fifty more than the entire recorded native flora. Most of these originated from Europe, particularly in imported grain from the eastern Mediterranean and the Black Sea. Others, such as Creeping Yellow Cress and Dyers' Greenweed are native in other parts of Britain, but are thought to be introduced ballast aliens at Aberdeen. A few American plants were recorded, and some of them such as Canadian Pondweed and the Blue Lupin, were spectacularly successful at establishing themselves. South America furnished only a few casuals, and Africa and Australia nothing at all. As Trail remarked, 'many of the European weeds, like the European nations, appear to have a peculiar power of annexing new lands into which they have come'.

The railway age is now almost over, at least as far as Aberdeen is concerned. Today it is the city's airport which is expanding rapidly. The Deeside line fell to Dr Beeching's axe in 1966, and within the city this once busy little line is now owned by Aberdeen District Council and converted into a public walkway. The flora of the branch line is no longer the cosmopolitan mixture recorded by Trail at the height of the railway age, for the native vegetation is returning. Even the disused stations are sprouting with the growth of ferns, mosses and rank grasses. As a result, the Old Deeside Line Walk has become an artery of greenery, stretching from King George VI Bridge through the ribbon-growth suburbs of Cults, Milltimber and Peterculter. Sycamore, ash, beech, wild cherry, wych elm, birch and willows have all established naturally and the banks contain a good variety of common grassland wild flowers, occasionally leavened by 'escapes' from the nearby gardens. These sunny banks are now among the best places near Aberdeen to see butterflies, and widespread species like Small Copper, Common Blue, Green-veined White and Meadow Brown are quite numerous. In one place there is even an inland colony of the much rarer Small Blue. The commoner thrushes, finches and warblers nest here, and the line provides the unwonted sight of Whitethroats singing from the whin bushes almost within a stone's throw of Guild Street station. The line is a 'natural' nature trail, and for my money, is one of the best of the City's public walks.

Chapter 3

The Concrete Jungle

THE MODERN TOWNSCAPE

The twentieth century contribution to the townscape has been dominated by the suburb and the roadway, with the occasional set-piece public building. The emphasis has nearly always been on utility, and the design of most of the post war suburbs can be most politely described as 'functional'. The most significant changes, which continue at an ever accelerating rate, have come to Aberdeen since Hitler's War, in the new age of planned growth. Between the wars, slum clearance removed much of the decaying fabric of the Victorian town, and genteel bungalows sprang up around the stately baronial mansions by the Dee, to create a long suburban sprawl as far out as Peterculter. In general, growth was leisurely. The earliest post-war civic satellite was Kincorth, which had been designed in 1938, but was delayed until 1946 by the war. Many of the new suburban houses which were built on the hillside above the Brig o' Dee continued to be faced with granite from Rubislaw: after all, Aberdeen was still the granite city, and it would have been unthinkable to use anything else. Alas, the supply and expense of granite were respectively too little and too much to match the giddy pace of post-war development. One of the first indications of the new age were the steam lorries, chugging up Aberdeen's hills with prefabricated houses on the back. Vast, maze-like suburbs developed on the bleak plateau west of Anderson Drive, all in the Corporation 'housing estate' style, which imposed a suburban uniformity from Penzance to Thurso. In the 1950s, veneers of granite were still used on a limited scale, but when Rubislaw Quarry closed in 1970, the supply ran out. The granite age was over.

In the early sixties, a new type of housing appeared, consisting of two story closes and ranks of tower flats. For fifteen years, these cubic horrors sprang up all over the city, the Council leading the way with that plate glass monolith, St Nicholas House. In contrast to the situation in so many other cities, Aberdeen's tower blocks have evidently been successful within their limitations - the city has not yet been forced to tear one down. The oil age brought a new vigour to Aberdeen's growth. Industrial estates have been established at Nigg and Dyce, and a new generation of suburbs and dormitory towns created to serve the developing city. The new suburbs are more diverse and stylistically adventurous than the old. The housing at Torry, for instance, has, from nearby vantage points, a distinctly middle-eastern appearance, with its flat roof tops and harled concrete fabric. Others, north of the Don, have chosen a Scandinavian look, with their wooden facing and forest-cabin design. The new Aberdeen has been planned as a cosmopolitan city which must, above all things, be up to date. The ultimate gesture in modernism was to twin the city with Houston, Texas, the fastest growing city in the western hemisphere. It is a sad reflection of contemporary municipal values that so much of Aberdeen's history has been sacrificed in the process: much of the site of the medieval city was bulldozed away for car parks and office blocks before archaeologists could investigate the ground and a great opportunity to uncover the past was lost. A massive development is currently being planned for the central city, which if it reaches fruition, will make all previous changes pale into insignificance. This is the Comprehensive Development Area which is to turn the George Street - St Nicholas Street district into a single huge shopping precinct, by an alliance between the District Council and a Dutch firm. A prospect which must make most perceptive Aberdonians tremble.

Old Aberdeen, in the meantime, has gone its own way, partly because most of it is now owned by the university. The science buildings are of the usual plate glass and concrete campus style, but the heart of the old town has been preserved and beautifully restored. Even the noisy thoroughfare of St Machar Drive and the tower blocks of Hillhead of Seaton have not entirely ruined the pleasures of the walk from Seaton Park to Kings College. Here at least, the impact of the twentieth century has been relatively subdued.

LIFE ON THE BUILDINGS:

One of the outstanding wildlife success stores of recent times and one which is, so far, unique to Aberdeen is that of the urban Oystercatcher. The 'Oyc' has often shown an ability to adapt to new environments, an ability which belies its clownish appearance and imbecile, piping song. Once an exclusively coastal bird, it has long since spread inland, at first nesting mostly on river shingles, but now equally at home on loch shores, gravel pits, arable fields and even open woodland. It was quick to exploit the ideal nesting conditions provided by the North Sea gas pumping stations, which are spaced at five mile intervals along the pipeline routes. In the gravel surfacing around the pumps, the Oycs found not only the perfect substrate on which to make their nest 'scrapes', but also a nearby chain-link fence to keep out any unwelcome intruders.

The Aberdeen Oycs went on to exploit what at first sight looks the least attractive nest site imaginable: the tower block. The spate of Cubist high-rise flats and office blocks provided for the Oyc what they have failed, in some cities at least, to provide for mankind - a pleasant place to live and comparatively safe from predators. The flat roofs of most of the tower blocks are covered with gravel for insulation, and its possibilities quickly caught the eye of some Daniel Boone among Oycs. The thin layer of roof gravel is not usually sufficient to allow a typical Oyc nest scrape, but the birds learned to collect up the gravel into a small mound, and scoop out a hollow in the top for their eggs.

The city Oycs feed by probing short grass with their sensitive orange bills for earthworms and leatherjackets, which have reached an artificially high level of abundance in mown grassland. Since a nearby food supply is needed for the growing chicks, the parent Oycs have tended to colonise buildings which are close to open grassy areas. Modern schools, with their flat tops and nearby playing fields are ideal for the purpose, and virtually every one now has it own nesting pair. Hospitals and certain university buildings with spacious surrounding lawns are also favoured sites. Alan Knox, who has made a special study of these birds, estimates the total number nesting on city buildings at about thirty pairs, although they appear to be steadily increasing. As a rule, the successful breeding Oycs utilise public buildings rather than blocks of flats, presumably because there is less likelihood of disturbance.

Fledgling Oycs have an unfortunate habit of marching straight off a roof before they can fly, and even when they survive this experience and are replaced by some kindly human being, they generally repeat the performance almost immediately. For this reason, the most successful sites seem to be those roofs which are surrounded by short walls, and from which the chick cannot easily escape until it is fully fledged and able to fly. These sites may also be less vulnerable to the plentiful Kestrels roving Aberdeen's skies in search of an easy snack.

A second bird which has attracted attention by nesting on Aberdeen's buildings is the Herring Gull, but in this case it is a habit which occurs in other parts of the country and dates from the 1920s. The first nests on north eastern buildings were seen in Peterhead in the 1950s, although the gull may have begun to nest un-noticed on warehouses around the Aberdeen docks at the same time. Strangely enough, none of Aberdeen's large and active population of birdwatchers reported the presence of house-nesting gulls until the mid 1960s, when young birds were seen on roofs in the John Street area. By the time Dr Bourne ascended St Nicholas House in 1978 to census the gull population, they were everywhere on old chimney stacks and high buildings throughout central Aberdeen, with outlying groups at Victoria Road, Woodend Hospital and the University Botany Department. The largest, and almost certainly the oldest, colony was centred on the dockyard warehouses near the railway station.

There is little doubt that it is the rich pickings from the harbour and open refuse tips like Tullos Hill, which have attracted the gulls to the city. With a permanent and guaranteed food supply on the doorstep, so to speak, the adult birds have less reason to move away from their nesting sites, and consequently their young continue to be brought food well after their cliff nesting congeners would have been left to fend for themselves. Dr Bourne suggests that this greatly increases the juvenile gulls' chances of surviving their first winter and that the urban nesting habit can therefore confer considerable advantages. As he drily remarks, 'the implications of this phenomenon for the future increase of town-nesting gulls hardly require elaboration.' As if to underline this point, a pair of Greater Black-backed Gulls have begun to hold territory on buildings near the docks, in much the same area as the first urban Herring Gulls are thought to have nested. It will be interesting to see if the Black-backs follow their example.

Unlike the Johnny-come-lately Oycs and gulls, the city must have had Kestrels nesting on its major buildings for centuries. Whereas the Oycs have exploited the latest architectural styles and the gulls show rather common tastes in Victoriana, Kestrels tend to be more refined. The twin spires of St Machar Cathedral, for instance, each have a well-known Kestrel's eyrie, and another well-known site is perched high among the neo-Gothic pinnacles of Marischal College. In general, tall towers, including disused chimneys, are favoured nesting sites, although at least one hospital has a pair nesting beneath its eaves. A recent survey of Aberdeen's urban Kestrels suggests that there are about twenty pairs within the built up area, five of them in Rubislaw Quarry alone. Like their congeners in other cities, they evidently feed mostly on birds, such as House Sparrows and Blackbirds, with fewer small mammals in their diet than the country birds. This means, unfortunately, that their breeding success tends to be poorer, because of an accumulation of pesticides from their prey. The insidious build up of toxic residues in birds of prey, sometimes with disastrous results, is one of the best documented facts of post-war natural history. Earthworms can store up large amounts of poisons, including lead from petrol fumes, without apparent ill-effect, and persistent poisons, harboured in the fatty tissue of the animal, are passed on up the food-chain: worms - Blackbirds - Kestrels.

A less subtle menace to Kestrels are boys who, having seen the film Kes, want a young Kestrel of their own. In most of the Aberdeen nesting sites, the risk to the boys is greater than to the Kestrel, but for the safety of both species most nesting sites are wisely kept secret.

The Black Redstart is famous as the one nationally rare bird which is an almost exclusively urban species. Aberdeen lies well to the north of its normal breeding range, although it regularly visits these shores as a summer visitor. It is possible, however, that the Black Redstart has nested in Aberdeen at least once, although it is not likely to have reared a clutch. Walking past some derelict buildings on Huntly Street, several years ago, Robert Rae, a leading local ornithologist, heard the loud and distinctive song of the Black Redstart from high among the ruins. At once he contacted his brother from a nearby phone booth and asked for a tape recording of the Black Redstart's song to be played over the telephone. This confirmed what Robert already suspected. A singing bird in nesting habitat during the breeding season, is good evidence that it might well be breeding in the area. Demolition work had already begun on the street, however, and so the pair hurried back to the site that same evening, to try to locate the nest. Alas, the demolition men had beaten them to it. The building, which may or may not have held Aberdeen's first Black Redstart nest, was a pile of rubble shimmering beneath a pall of dust.

The Pied Wagtail behaves in an opposite way to the Black Redstart, for it is a rural bird in the summer, returning to the centre of the town in the winter months. In summer, most of Aberdeen's birds roost communally in one of two relatively wild places by the Don and the Dee respectively. Around November, however, many Pied Wagtails return to the city and gather on the roof of the railway station. Up to five hundred birds use this site as a roost in early winter.

Aberdeen's population of bats appear, so far as is known, to roost entirely in buildings, and this seems to be a characteristic of the north east as a whole. Aberdeen's bats have undergone a curious change-over of species since they were first investigated in the mid-nineteenth century. William MacGillivray's paper to the Edinburgh Philosophical Journal in 1844, entitled 'Description of Vespertilio Daubentonii (the Daubenton's Bat) from specimens found in Aberdeenshire', is among the first publications to describe the natural history of Aberdeen city. At that time, the Daubenton's Bat was apparently 'by far the most common and abundant bat we have', and several hundreds used to roost inside the roof of Old St Machar Cathedral. By 1891 however, when George Sim climbed up to the rafters to look for himself, all the bats had gone. Sim attributed this to a recent roof renovation, and its effect has been permanent: there are no known Daubenton's Bat roosts in Aberdeen today, and far from being the commonest north eastern bat, it is now the most rare.

The Pipistrelle on the other hand, seems to be much commoner now than in the past. Sim regarded it as scarce, although he noted several sightings from Waterton Paper Works. From that precarious basis, the north east has become something of a national Pipistrelle stronghold: Paul Racey of the University Zoology Department regards Deeside as one of the best concentrations of Pipistrelle summer roosts in Britain, although the bats evidently migrate southwards for the winter. The Pipistrelle is an animal of suburban houses in Aberdeen; no roosts have yet been found in the city centre. It is regularly seen in the High Street of Old Aberdeen however. Unlike the Daubenton's and Long-eared Bats which roost in the points of a roof, the Pipistrelle squeezes itself into narrow crannies and might therefore be less prone to disturbance.

The foregoing species have all made an adaptative change from rural to urban life, whether from cliffs to roof tops and spires like the Herring Gull and Kestrel, from shingle to the gravelly tops of tower blocks like the Oystercatcher, or from caves and hollow trees to the rafters, like the bats. These are the opportunitists, the hitchhikers riding on mankind's affluence, and they have become almost as urban as a stockbroker. The built up areas of cities sometimes provide the unexpected, however. Occasionally animals which are thoroughly rural and have made little accomodation towards man's way of life, turn up in unexpected places. This may take the form of an accident of migration, such as the White's Thrush which was seen at the Castlehill Barracks or the Spotted Crake found dead in Guild Street, both in 1916, or the Lesser Grey Shrike in a chimney at Footdee in 1952 (see page 116). Sometimes there may be a purpose behind the visit, such as the Stoats which have been known to invade the abbatoirs, although the behaviour of the Brown Hares which used to lope along Aberdeen's tram rails in the spring must presumably be ascribed to March madness.

So far, we have confined our attentions to relatively large mammals and birds and to the city's more distinctive buildings. The everyday wildlife of house and home is a smaller world and a more intimate one. Most forms of household wildlife are not welcomed by the occupiers, who are often prepared to take pains to get rid of them. A list of insects of the city, compiled in 1905, begins with '*Pulex irritans*. Human Flea. On Man.' The human flea is said to be a great rarity, these days, and modern suburban houses are certainly sterile abodes for domestic wildlife, compared with the rambling Victorian manors. No detailed survey of the wildlife of domestic houses has ever taken place in Aberdeen, so far as I am aware - this is the domain of the pest control officer and rat-catcher, rather than the naturalist. In any case, the results would be unlikely to show any significant difference between Aberdeen's domestic wildlife and that of any other British city. Since their surroundings are controlled by thermostat, rather than the vagaries of the weather, domestic animals tend to be cosmopolitan. I would recommend their study to school children and students: a survey of the school caretaker's house, for instance, would be of great educational value. It would reveal a new world literally at one's feet, which is usually over-looked: Window Fly larvae preying on Carpet Beetles, insects that gnaw metal and chew tobacco, tiny Pseudo-Scorpions stalking the family Encyclopaedia for Book Lice. To identify such beasts, I recommend a thoroughly alarming book called Collins Guide to Wildlife in House and Home.

Many domestic insects and invertebrates are foreigners, which are unable to survive in Scotland except in artificially heated surroundings. A well known example is the House Cricket, which used to be commoner in the days of open kitchen hearths. It is more often to be heard today on refuse tips, which generate their own heat through decomposition, but a colony lives around the heating ducts in the University Zoology Department, having escaped from captive stock. The tiny yellowish Pharoah Ant prefers the student Halls of Residence, where they are harmless, if annoying, neighbours. They become a more serious pest in hospitals; where they can become distributors of disease unless controlled.

Some of the more exotic domestic invertebrates are accidental imports. Perhaps the oddest example recorded from Aberdeen was a handsome Scandinavian wood-boring beetle, *Tetropium fuscum*, which hatched out of a hole in an imported pepper-pot! Such occurences are rare, and unlikely to result in a local breeding colony, but one unlikely invertebrate appears to have become well-established in one of Aberdeen District Council's building and works department properties. This is the scorpion. Scorpions have been seen here on a sufficiently large number of occasions over a period of time, to suggest that they have probably formed a temporary colony. The species has not yet been identified, but it is probably the same one as the small, fairly harmless scorpion which is established in parts of London. If so, I hope the Council leave them alone. Their sting is not much worse than that of a bee, and their occasional appearances must make an agreeable diversion during a dull day's work.

LIFE IN THE GARDEN

When one walks through the back door into the garden, one passes abruptly from one 'artificial' habitat into another. Unlike that of the house, the wildlife of the garden has to put up with Aberdeen's natural climate but, on the other hand, there are ready benefits to be derived from the cornucopia of flowers, vegetables, bird tables, shrubberies and dust bins in Aberdeen's well-managed gardens. It has become one of the truisms of conservation parlance that gardens are one of the last and richest refuges for wildlife and, like most truisms, this is not altogether true. The contrast between a large, leafy, well-established old garden, full of rough corners, and that of the pocket-handkerchief of lawn which is all that one gets with most modern houses, is on a par with that between a nature reserve and a town park. In an aggregate sense, gardens *are* important, however. Eighty four percent of Edinburgh's million trees are in private gardens (one might expect a much lower proportion in Aberdeen, although no comparable figures are available). One famous garden in Leicestershire yielded a total of over five hundred species of Ichneumon wasps - more than in any known nature reserve. Part of the reason for this is the garden's incredible diversity - an old ivy-covered wall, a garden pond, a mass of traditional flowers and shrubs, and a few old trees, together cram far more variety within the small space of a garden than is ever likely to happen in nature.

Garden insects are more often the subject of a gardener's wrath than of a naturalist's curiosity. One exception is the moth fauna of the suburban garden of a modern house in Dyce, which has been studied and recorded in detail over the past eleven years. The householder, Robert Palmer, a leading local entomologist, has listed the remarkable total of two hundred and seventy seven species of moth from this small garden, of which seventy three are small 'micros', and the remainder . 'macros' or larger moths. To most people, these may be surprisingly large figures; nor is there anything especially unusual about this particular garden: two to three hundred moths is probably the 'going rate' of many a suburban garden near Aberdeen, although not all these moths would necessarily breed there. When Robert Palmer acquired his house, the garden was open to the surrounding countryside. Since then it has been engulfed by new housing, and Robert estimates that twenty or thirty species may have been 'lost' as a result. The more interesting moths on his list include the Sallow Kitten and the Puss Moth, both of which owe their presence to a Sallow bush at the bottom of the garden. A micro-moth, *Lobesia littoralis*, which is normally confined to the coast, occurs here since Robert grows its food-plant, Thrift, in his rockery. A crop of currant bushes in one corner forms the home of at least three moths of the Geometer family, the Phoenix, the V-moth, and that well-known town species, the Magpie Moth. Colourful and incidentally, quite harmless garden residents include a good selection of the beautifully burnished Plusia moths, with names like the Gold Spot and the Gold Spangle, and the lovely Garden Tiger-moth with its hairy 'woolly bear' caterpillars. A Buddleia bush attracts Small Tortoiseshell and Red Admiral butterflies, and it had its fair share of visiting Painted Ladies, during that butterfly's exceptional immigration of 1980 (q.v.).

Of the 'unofficial' flowers which find their way into gardens, the majority are annuals, which maintain a precarious existence in well-weeded flower beds, but spread with explosive speed if these are neglected for long. At least two wild flowers, the Petty Spurge and the Persian Speedwell seem, in fact, to be found more often in gardens than anywhere else. On well-mown lawns, a second species of speed-well, the Round-Leaved, is now common. This Turkish plant has spread rapidly throughout Britain since 1927, but since it never ripens its seeds here, it probably owes its abundance to continual introductions from lawn grass seed mixtures.

Although relatively few wild flowers spread into small gardens, there are a great many garden flowers which travel in the opposite direction. These are the garden escapes, whose successful break-outs now swell the pages of the British Floras. Sometimes the escape is aided by man. One example which is especially characteristic of Aberdeen, is the Blue Sow-thistle, which many gardeners initially find attractive until they discover the plant's drawbacks. The Sow-thistle spreads rapidly because of its muscular creeping root system, and it can quickly take over a flower bed, smothering the other growth with its rank leaves. Once it has changed from an asset to a pest, it is generally ripped up and thrown out. Where its remains have been flung, it some-times grows up again, like the broomstick of the Sorcerer's Apprentice, and this is probably the reason why it occurs on roadsides and neglected places around Aberdeen. An equally successful escape from the garden to similar places in and around the city is the pretty Spurred Violet, *Viola cornuta*.

An interesting variation on this theme was the Maryculter House Incident. A walled garden on the west side of the house was the site of

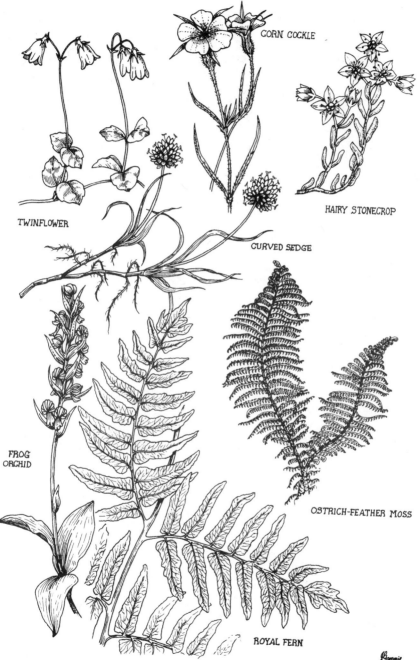

Fig. 3. Lost or vanishing plants around Aberdeen.

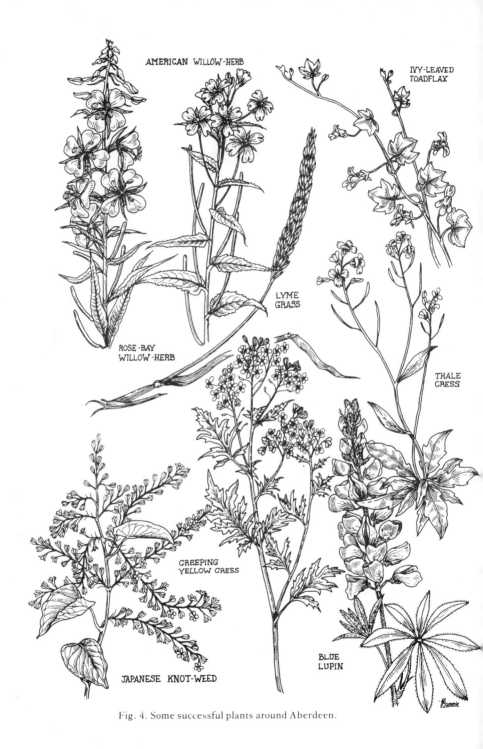

AMERICAN WILLOW-HERB

IVY-LEAVED TOADFLAX

LYME GRASS

ROSE-BAY WILLOW-HERB

THALE CRESS

CREEPING YELLOW CRESS

BLUE LUPIN

JAPANESE KNOT-WEED

Fig. 4. Some successful plants around Aberdeen.

a medieval herb garden, owned and cultivated by the Knights Hospitaller. In 1936, the long-neglected old garden was gutted and the plant remains thrown out over the wall. There was, unfortunately, no botanist present to list an inventory of the garden, but it is unlikely to be mere coincidence that below the wall is one of the few north eastern sites for a plant mentioned in all medieval herbals, the Cuckoo-Pint.

In spatial terms, the largest garden 'micro-habitat' is the lawn. Foreigners regard our obsession with lawns as faintly dotty and peculiarly British: mown, weeded, cossetted with sand and weedkiller, our lawns require as much maintenance as an agricultural crop. Only the toughest weeds survive in a properly maintained lawn, and few animals live permanently on its surface. There is plenty going on underneath the green carpet, however; up to twenty million Nematode worms and ten thousand mites are found in every cubic yard of topsoil, quite apart from lesser, but nonetheless still astronomical, numbers of earthworms, leather-jackets and assorted grubs. This rich potential larder is exploited by many birds. Some, such as the Blackbird, Song Thrush or Robin may nest nearby, provided there is suitable shrub cover. Others like the Starling or Jackdaw might nest under the eaves or on the roof of the house. The Collared Dove is an example of a recent arrival which appears to have exploited an available suburban 'niche' and often appears on lawns along with the Sparrows and Starlings.

A large number of observations have been made of Blackcaps on bird tables in suburban gardens in recent years, and Aberdeen has one of the greatest reported number of instances where these summer visitors have overwintered. The broad-leaved woodlands of the city provide extensive areas of nesting habitat for Blackcaps (and for another warbler, the Chiffchaff), and if bird table produce becomes a regular source of food, there is no reason why they should not continue to increase. In that event, we should count our blessings, because the song of the Blackcap is comparable only with that of the Nightingale.

An interesting future possibility in Aberdeen's larger gardens may be the Fieldfare. This large thrush, normally a winter visitor, first bred in Britain in 1967, and several pairs now nest in scattered localities in Aberdeenshire, one of them not far from the city. In Stockholm, the Fieldfare is a familiar bird of parks and gardens, and since Aberdeen lies in the same latitude, it is, perhaps, a bird to look out for.

A bird which has made a welcome return to Aberdeen's gardens and parks in recent years is the Goldfinch. This Harlequin of the finch family was ruthlessly exploited by cagebird fanciers in the nineteenth century, as were other finches and larks. By 1900, George Sim feared that the Goldfinch was nearing extinction in Deeside and Aberdeen, two of the last nesting pairs having been trapped near Rubislaw Quarry in 1894. For over seventy years, Goldfinches were rarely seen in Aberdeen, but they have made a steady recovery in the past ten years and are fairly common in parts of the city. Illegal 'liming' for attractive song birds has not ceased altogether, unfortunately, and incidents continue to be reported almost annually.

Few would regard the arrival of the Grey Squirrel, also in the last decade, with the same unalloyed pleasure. Its presence at Aberdeen does not seem to be generally known, and it may be of interest to look back at how it got here. Contrary to their usual suburban avenues of spread, the first north eastern Grey Squirrels were seen in hill regions. One was shot in Glen Tanar in the winter of 1970-71, and others were identified with certainty at the same time in the Glen Dye and Ballogie area. Shortly afterwards, the squirrel turned up on a garden bird table in the Aberdeen suburb of Mannofield. From that point onwards, the Scottish Woodland Owners Association thought it advisable to keep a tally of sightings of this potential menace, and Dr Brian Staines of the Institute of Terrestrial Ecology in Banchory has built up a dossier on the squirrel's status in the north east. Since 1972, infrequent but regular sightings have been made in suburban Aberdeen, where the squirrel evidently inhabits gardens and broad-leaved policy woodlands. It has been seen at Hazlehead and some other parks, but only on rare occasions. Dr Staines now believes that the Grey Squirrel is resident in small numbers at Aberdeen.

So far as one is able to judge from isolated sightings, the Grey Squirrel appears to have leap-frogged over the Grampians, but failed to build up its numbers once it arrived in the lowlands. It has recently repeated this peculiar pattern by popping up from nowhere in Elgin and the Moray Firth area. The possibility of its sudden appearances being due to zoo escapes has been discounted and it is more likely that it is under-recorded and keeping an unusually low profile. Whether or not the Grey Squirrel is on the brink of becoming a familiar animal around Aberdeen and, if so, whether it will have an adverse effect on our broad-leaved woodlands and the native Red Squirrel, remains to be seen.

LIFE IN THE STREETS

Rubislaw Terrace gives as good an example as any of the natural history of a Victorian street and, since the Nature Conservancy Council acquired an office there in 1978, its wildlife has been fairly well recorded. This smart granite terrace was completed in 1852 by a local architect James Giles, during Aberdeen's Abbotsford House period, when the prevailing aim seemed to be to make every new building look as much like Sir Walter Scott's house as possible. The novelist, Baron

Corvo, who once lived nearby, rather unkindly called Rubislaw Terrace a row of 'granite rabbit hutches.' A balustrade runs along the elaborate frontage, and is separated from the main road by a strip of grass with trees, flower beds, and a central concrete pool, over which a fountain occasionally plays. It is the epitome of Victorian Aberdeen (Victoria herself presides over it at Queen's Cross), although what was then a fashionable residential neighbourhood is now give over to offices and hotels.

The NCC office at number 17 is typical of the terrace. Barely a blade of grass grows within its precincts, since the old back yard and out-building were demolished to make way for a car park. Nonetheless, a surprisingly large and diverse number of animals and plants have found ways of surviving. Three or four pairs of Swifts regularly dis-appear under the eaves each summer, and somewhere on the roof, probably behind the chimney stack, must be an urban Herring Gull's nest, since unfledged chicks have been spotted running about. A Sparrowhawk flies over from time to time, and has displayed nearby, although the nearest breeding site is probably Hazlehead. Outside, on the branch of a lonely, stunted Sycamore tree, there sometimes perches a Tawny Owl, and a Woodcock has been seen flashing past, on its way, presumably, to some far off boggy brake. In autumn, pass-ages of geese fly in formation overhead, and Oystercatchers are fre-quent visitors, although the nearest nesting site is some little distance away.

It is when we turn to the local wildflowers however that we find the neatest adaptations to the conditions of an urban street. Fronting the terrace is a line of mature trees, including some fine Wych Elms. The green sward below the trees is destitute: search as I might, I found nothing there but sown grass, daisies and the inevitable pigeons. But the crevices and nooks in the granite paving stones and building fabric of the terrace are full of interest. Urban stonework is hardly an inviting habitat, even when left alone by man: drought, violent change and lack of soil eliminate all but the best plant strategists. The most obvious adaptation is that taken by the annuals, which splurge out vast quant-ities of seed, like a firework, before fizzling up and dying when their meagre water supply dries up. This gives them a good chance of finding and colonising any bare patch or cranny which becomes available. Apart from the ubiquitous weeds such as groundsel and chickweed, the annual I most associate with the terrace is Thale Cress. This little spring Crucifer formerly grew on dry banks and turf walls in this neighbourhood, before the advance of the city swept them away. Professor Trail had found it a rather scarce flower at the beginning of the century, but now it grows in profusion, particularly in mossy cracks between the pavement and the iron railings of the houses, and each slender tap-root lies firmly embedded in a tiny pocket of soil.

The damp wall-tops and the open basements fronting each terraced house are the province of the willow-herbs. Mosses colonise the walls first, and accumulate a thin soil, while they also act as a water-retaining sponge. Willow-herbs proliferate in such places, wherever the soil is damp enough, and at Rubislaw, the native species have been more or less replaced by a swarthy North American relative, *Epilobium adenocaulon*. This species, which has arrived too recently to have attracted a generally used common name, was not known in Britain before 1891, and it reached Aberdeen at some unknown date since. Quite why it has been such a success is not easy to determine, but it shares all the peculiar willow-herb attributes to a marked degree: it combines the longevity of a perennial with the stupendous seed production of an annual; moreover it is a very 'plastic' plant, capable of growing in a bewildering array of shapes and sizes. Finally, it has to perfection what all urban wild flowers must have: indestructability. No matter how thoroughly one weeds the gravel or clears the stonework, this American Willow-herb comes bouncing back again: *adenocaulon* is here to stay.

Its companion in the basements is that pretty climber with miniature Snapdragon flowers known as Ivy-Leaved Toadflax. It has adorned British walls since 1640, when it was probably introduced from the Mediterranean, but both Dickie (1860) and Trail (1923) regarded it as rather rare, although the latter added that 'it had become plentiful on garden walls in Rubislaw Den House.' Sixty years later, it abounds, filling the less disturbed basements with its luxuriant polka dot foliage, and sprouting out of every available chink in the walls. The secret of its success must lie in its unusual means of propagation. The seed-containing capsules are held on long stalks, which bend away from strong light. This delivers the capsules into dark cracks in the walls, where the seeds are shed in the place which offers them the best chance to germinate.

At least two other wall plants found on the terrace appear to have increased since Trail's day: the delicate Lady Fern, which could have been deliberately planted, and Yellow Corydalis, a garden escape of long-standing. It is intriguing to speculate why all these plants should be doing so well. It is probably because there are more gaps than formerly in the fabric of Victorian Aberdeen, where 'unofficial' plants can gain a purchase. When Trail was active, the Victorian walls and pavements were comparatively new, and devoid of plant life. Time has matured Rubislaw Terrace and the granite is gently cracking apart like a ripe cheese. A second possible reason suggests itself: when the area was a residential neighbourhood, the basements and backyards would have been well-scrubbed and in constant use. With the takeover of the terrace by the nine till five business world, they have become redundant, ignored and overgrown.

Some Aberdeen wall plants have been less proficient at spreading themselves. The Wall Rue Spleenwort fern, which is common on granite walls in Aboyne and other places on Deeside, is unaccountably rare, apart from on a few walls in Old Aberdeen. And whatever has happened to all those Fooses or House Leeks which used to be planted out on old roof slates in the city, as protection from heavenly fire? Did people stop believing in its supernatural powers? Perhaps the least successful of all has been the Wall Pennywort, so familiar to children and botanists on the west coast, but absent in the north east except for two old walls at the edge of the City District, where, despite the passage of a century or more, it has stuck and failed to spread an inch further.

Chapter 4

The Green Islands

In one sense the whole city is an urban park. As if to compensate for the overall greyness of Aberdeen's granite buildings and matching climate, the main roads and city centre are draped and saturated with crocuses, daffodils and roses whose seasonal colour gleams like fresh paint. The City Parks Department received the ultimate accolade for its efforts by retiring undefeated from the Britain in Bloom competition in order to give some other town a chance of winning. Such magnificent swathes of colour of course require careful tending. To keep Aberdeen in bloom requires the effort of forty foreman-supervisors, seven district supervisors, ten technical advisors and a small army of parks staff all mowing, pruning and manicuring the land into obedience. If there is an unwritten slogan which motivates this highly accomplished band, it is Tidiness, Colour, Safety. The emphasis of their management is on intensive maintenance, as the Parks Convenor makes clear in the official booklet: 'because so many people enjoy (the parks), they are maintained to a high standard and the Parks Committee seek to make them interesting and pleasant places to be.' And pleasant for human beings and tulips they undoubtedly are but, as a result,they tend also to be rather hostile places for wildlife.

The oldest open space in the city is undoubtedly the coastal Links, the traditional playground of generations of Aberdonians. In the seventeenth century, football, archery, bowling and of course golf were all practised on what was then natural duneland, and the same area was also used for the regular call-to-arms and military training sessions. The line of sands between Donmouth and the Dee formed a two mile point to point, later superseded by a circular race track below Broad Hill. The first area to be officially designated as an urban park was the Play Green, which is marked on Parson Gordon's map as a square plot of land between the Gilcomston Burn and the New Town Loch. This was a traditional meeting place as early as the fifteenth century, when the Master of Civic Revels arranged 'dramas and processions' - probably local versions of Medieval morality plays. The popularity of the Play Green originated from the health-giving waters of a Spa well near the Gilcomston Burn, and it was a campaign in 1635 by a local artist, George Jameson, to preserve the well from flooding, which led to the official civic designation of the area as a park. The land later became the site of a hospital and Aberdeen's first park now lies buried beneath a different and less attractive type of park: the Denburn underground car park. A rather charming early eighteenth century version of the Spa Well has been reconstructed there recently by John Souter of the City Department of Planning, although the Spa waters would no longer be conducive to good health.

Below the Play Green, the Denburn passed through a defile known as Corby Heugh, on its way down to the Dee estuary. The area between the Heugh and the main gateway to the burgh at the Green was common pasture land until 1757, when a series of improvements were made which provided this area with many characteristics of an urban park although it was never designated as such. This area combined a utilitarian and an amenity function. A public bleaching green and bathhouse were laid out in pleasant surroundings with planted trees, and the burn itself was channelled into a series of ornamental cascades. Although the course of the burn later became used as a track for the Inverness railway, the gardens live on as Union Terrace Gardens.

No further progress was made for over a century: open country lay no more than half a mile away and there was no particular need for any more urban parks until the unprecedented expansion of the granite city in the boom years of the mid-nineteenth century. Escape from the smoke and noise of the new industrial era became more and more difficult, and the new circumstances demanded havens of greenery within the city itself. In 1871, the Town Council responded by acquiring thirteen acres of common pasture at the outskirts of the city, known as Glennie's Park, and converted it into an area specifically designed for the leisure of the masses, according to Victorian precepts. An elaborate fountain was erected, rectangular flower beds were dug, trees were planted, vulgar sports like football were banned and the first Victorian Park came into existence. It was followed by a spate of others over the next thirty years; first Union Terrace Gardens in 1872 on the site of the old bleaching green, then the large and important Duthie Park by the Dee, which was gifted to the City in 1881. A Public Parks Department was set up in 1878 to administer the new parks, and two more had been added by the turn of the century: Stewart Park in 1894, and Westburn Park in 1901.

These parks all followed the Victorian pattern: rigid formalism, a high degree of maintenance and a generous sprinkling of ostentatious ornaments: obelisks, fountains, bandstands, Corinthian columns, Gothic ruins, whalebone arches and drinking wells.

After the Victorian extravaganzas there was a pause. The second wave of urban parks introduced a greater stress on informal recreation, reflecting the changing twentieth century attitudes towards leisure. When, in a far-sighted move, the City bought back part of its old Freedom Lands at Hazelhead in 1920 for a public open space, they were purchasing what was then open country. Johnstone Gardens became, in 1936, the first park within the city to be designed along informal lines. Its rustic bridges, water gardens and rockeries required as high a degree of maintenance as any of the earlier parks, but it was one step away from the endless lawns and geometrical flower beds which formed the *sine qua non* of the earlier parks. Groups of mature beeches and sycamores were left standing which provided a more natural, sylvan setting. The same blend of formal gardens and informal woodland and riverine walks characterised the large park at Seaton in Old Aberdeen, which was purchased in 1947.

The urban parkland forms a spectrum of maintenance ranging in its intensity from the rose gardens and flower beds of Anderson Drive at one extreme, to the multi-purpose, semi-wild park of Hazlehead at the other. The formal parks are physically very similar to a 'formal' private garden, enlarged in area but scarcely in variety. In consequence, they share much the same wildlife, although 'wild' is scarcely an appropriate word. For these parks are almost as far removed from natural conditions as their surrounding concrete and tarmacadam. They are monocultures of sown grass, managed in rather the same way and at the same intensity as a crop of oats. Any animal or plant that dwells in them unbidden must be capable of adapting to very heavy public pressure and a high degree of maintenance. The expanses of lawns are a feeding area for a number of birds, since vast numbers of earthworms, leather jackets and moth larvae are present beneath the crop of grass. Gulls, rooks, and a variety of song birds may feed on the turf but they nest elsewhere. The nesting birds of the parks depend on finding relatively undisturbed shrubberies, trees and secluded corners. In general, the more of these there are, the greater the density and variety of nesting bird life.

As a habitat for wild flowers, the parks are even worse. The only plants on the lawns are those which can compete against the vigorous competition of sown grass and can withstand regular mowing. These are mostly limited to daisies, yarrows and a scattering of hawkbits, the 'middle class' plants as they have been called[1] of grass-verge-and-private-garage districts. Such areas are botanically about as poor as they can be: green concrete. The woody plants, too, are entirely planted and mostly foreign, and harbour no more than a tiny fraction of the wild-life of our indigenous trees. Even the numerous mature beeches and sycamores are introductions and are dull, deadly dull, compared with the life supported by a well grown oak, ash or birch tree. Above all, it is the parks authority's obsession with tidiness which sweeps away most of the possible refuges for wildlife: no dead standing or lying timber, no ponds apart from concrete paddling pools, no neglected corners where nettles and harmless weeds could harbour breeding Small Tortoiseshell butterflies or food for nesting finches. It is this lack of small-scale variation which robs these green islands of what they *could* support, and that is why municipal parks are usually barren in wildlife terms, compared with many so-called waste places.

These are of course generalisations, and some of the parks do have a greater diversity of wildlife than others. The poorest are the old Victorian parks, but even this statement needs qualification. In Duthie Park, for instance, there is a fine dawn and evening chorus of songbirds which implies a reasonably high density of some birds at least. Closer inspection shows that what these birds may gain in volume, they lack in diversity. The choir is composed of little more than the Chaffinch, Song Thrush and that supreme park species, the Blackbird. Indeed the Blackbird was probably quite rare in Aberdeen before the nineteenth century parks and suburban gardens provided it with the ideal combination of short grass for feeding and shrubberies for nesting. It is more instructive to recount the members of the choir which are missing. If some grass were left unmown until late summer, Skylarks and, probably, Meadow Pipits would nest, as they do in similar but unmown grassland owned by BP in Dyce. If untidy corners were left where chickweeds, thistles, willow-herb and nettles and their associated insects could survive, we would see more Linnets, Greenfinches and Goldfinches.

Two bird stories may be of relevance here. The longest grass in the city parks at bird nesting time is in the beds of daffodils, which are not cut until well after the flowers have died. The daffodil season is often late enough at Seaton Park to attract incoming Willow Warblers to nest in what looks to them like ideal long grass. The result is predictable: when the last of the daffodils are over, the motor mowers roar into action and there then commences what has been dubbed 'the Annual Willow Warbler Massacre'. In fairness to the men behind the mowing machines

1   W G Teagle, The Endless Village.

it is unlikely that they are aware that they are chopping up anything except grass, but, as the unlucky Willow Warblers demonstrate, seemingly innocent hosts of golden daffodils can also be baited traps for wild birds.

A second Seaton Park story illustrates the park's potential as a bird refuge under certain circumstances. Some years ago, part of the central corridor of planted shrubberies at Seaton was allowed to become overgrown and gently dishevelled in appearance. As a result, it became a veritable avian Hilton Hotel. At one time, the shrubbery held a breeding colony of Redpolls, a significant percentage of the city's nesting Goldfinches and, in 1977, the first breeding pair of Lesser Whitethroats ever recorded north of the Forth. Unfortunately, the riches of these bushes attracted a bird ringer whose persistent attempts to catch and ring the birds with a mist net attracted, in turn, the attention of a park keeper. That bird ringer, he decided, was a nuisance, and the bush, he noticed, badly needed pruning: shortly afterwards the best part of the shrubbery had been cut back to such an extent that a passing Blackbird would scarcely have glanced at it. The moral seems to be that bird ringers should be circumspect in city parks, and preferably on good terms with the local parks staff.

But urban parks are not, of course, intended to be nature reserves. They are designed to cater for human beings or, to be more precise, to the municipal authority's view of what human beings require in their leisure hours. Birds and birdsong are obviously part of that need, but it may not matter very much which particular kinds of birds are present, just so long as there are *birds*, moving about and twittering. The cheerful song and coy stance of Blackbirds, Thrushes and Robins suit the requirement precisely, and if the townsman requires more variety, he can always go to the well-stocked aviary at Hazlehead. Nor are there pressing *conservation* grounds for suggesting that untidy places or bits of wet ground should be kept aside for Linnet or Redshank. It can hardly make any difference to Britain's Linnet population whether they nest in Aberdeen's parks or not. But does the absence of Linnets in Aberdeen's parks make any difference to *us*? Does not some atavistic urge make us long to see more wildlife, going about their business blissfully unaware of inflation, unemployment and race riots, in the very heart of a modern city? The conservation argument could, with greater justification, be applied to the parks themselves. Duthie Park must be one of the finest Victorian parks in Scotland, a fragment of the past as significant and impressive in its way, as an old pine forest or Craigievar Castle. Perhaps on these grounds it deserves the enormous expense of managing it in an old-fashioned way. But with understanding and imaginative planning, there is surely room for Victorian parkland and

Linnets at Duthie Park, providing that its managers can be convinced that both are assets.

Two larger birds not traditionally associated with towns have benefitted from the city's parks and green spaces. The first is the Magpie, which now nests throughout the city in parks, rough ground and allotments, wherever there is suitable tree cover. Magpies moved into the suburbia of several large cities in the 1940s, but Aberdeen's birds are some of the most thoroughly urban. In view of their status as common town birds in Norway and Sweden, the Magpie's success in comparable climes at Aberdeen is particularly interesting. There is a strong possibility that they were drawn into the city as a refuge, since they are relentlessly persecuted in the country.

Aberdeen's other urban Corvid, the Rook, has a much longer pedigree as an Aberdonian bird. The Corbies of Corbie Heugh, the old braes of the Denburn, were probably Rooks, and rookeries there still are in the trees of Union Terrace Gardens, in the very heart of the city. Elsewhere in the city there are larger rookeries, which authorities have tried unsuccessfully to eliminate from time to time, with the biggest of all in the wooded braes of the Don, near the Brig o' Balgownie. The worms and leatherjackets in the short cropped turf of the parks must provide a lucrative source of food.

The 'informal' parks like Johnstone Gardens and the more rural parts of Hazlehead and Seaton have areas of mixed woodland which attract birds not normally seen in the central parks. The Sparrowhawk is probably the most glamorous of these, but the Stock Dove is sometimes seen at Seaton, and these parks generally support a greater number and variety of finches and tits. Let us leave Seaton's woods aside for the moment (since they properly belong to the section devoted to the Don valley) and home in on Hazlehead.

HAZLEHEAD

With the possible exception of the Don valley, the richest wildlife refuge in Aberdeen is Hazlehead. This green enclave on the western edge of the city is large enough to be managed on a pattern of multi-purpose use containing both intensively managed formal gardens and nurseries, and informal woodland walks. As a result, Hazlehead is neither a wholly urban park nor quick-frozen countryside like the true Country Parks, but something in between. Wildlife is one of its amenities, and the District Department of Leisure and Recreation have designed two nature trails, one long and the other short, through the more interesting parts. An illustrated booklet describes some of the features which the walker is intended to see.

The importance of Hazlehead resides mainly in its trees, which together with those of the Don valley, forms the largest area of broad-leaved woodland close to the city. The woods form a perimeter surrounding the central playing fields, golf course, riding stables and nurseries, with long ribbons of shelter belts chequering the park and providing a continuity of greenery. The woodland is not, of course, the least bit natural, but, and more important in this context, it is well-matured and contains large portions of relatively undisturbed mixed broadleaves. This provides a sylvan setting for some very non-urban wildlife.

Hazlehead was already well-wooded when it was bought from the Rose family by the Town Council, in 1920. Its policies included exotic trees such as three giant Sequoias, planted on the birth of successive Rose daughters, a walnut, a cedar and some Monkey Puzzles. Den Wood and the wilder parts of the park are more natural woodland of beech grading into mixed rowan and birch thickets, although plantations of exotic conifers intrude. Beech is by far and away the most widely planted broad-leaf in the Aberdeen area, both for shelter belts and nursery trees and, latterly, for timber. Beech is traditionally regarded in northern Scotland as an alien, which would have been absent from the original forests. However this may be, Aberdeen is certainly within the climatic tolerance of beech, because the tree regenerates well, far outstripping such avowedly native trees as oak or hazel. It has been widely planted for at least two hundred years, and has become so thoroughly naturalised that it is often impossible to say whether a tree is of planted or naturally regenerated origin. The ecologist A S Watt considered that north eastern beech behaves exactly as though it were a native tree, and has developed a natural woodland ground flora. Unfortunately the orchids and other interesting plants which characterise the beechwoods of the south are absent from the north east. The ground flora of the woods at Hazlehead grows on acidic soils and is botanically rather dull with grassland and brambles relieved, here and there, by wetter patches and leafy swards of Greater Wood-rush.

The conifers at Hazlehead occur in mixed stands with broad-leaves, and as monocultures. Larch and Scots Pine are both abundant, and Hazlehead is said to be the only place near Aberdeen where the latter regenerates naturally. Parts of Hazlehead would have almost certainly been under pine in prehistoric times, but it is unlikely that the present pines are their direct descendents. This was also the nearest place to the city where wild juniper bushes used to occur; Juniper is nearly always an indicator of relatively undisturbed woodland. The Sitka Spruces of the park are, of course, wholly exotic and introduced for their value as timber, rather than as an amenity. The District Council have now discontinued the planting of Sitka and plan to replace it gradually with beech.

Hazlehead has for over a century been the last retreat or, alternatively, the first toehold, of woodland animals whose natural ranges are changing. The Badger, for instance, became very scarce in the latter half of the nineteenth century through persecution, but it hung on at Hazlehead until 1874, when the last two were found drowned in a waterlade in which they had taken refuge. The Red Squirrel, on the other hand, first reappeared at Hazlehead in around 1855, after a long absence, and the mixed woodlands of the park continue to be one of its strongholds near Aberdeen.

At Hazlehead one at last begins to find a diverse range of birds. There are two woodpeckers, the Great Spotted which nests here and the Green which probably doesn't; three owls, the Barn, Tawny and Long-eared; and song birds such as Redpoll, Siskin and Long-tailed Tit. In the winter, Bramblings often congregate in the park to feed on beech mast, whilst, in some years at least, Waxwings can be seen shrilling around the Cotoneaster berries in the more 'formal' areas. The summer visitors include a medley of warblers - Blackcap, Whitethroat, Willow Warbler, as well as Spotted Flycatcher.

The bird one might least expect to find so close to a city, however, is the Capercaillie. It would be difficult to think of a less urban bird than this elusive wild turkey. One however, was reported in 1915 to have flown into the Aberdeen Central Post Office, and another at that time must have created still more alarm when it blundered into the theatre on Guild Street! Our last native Capers became extinct in around 1785, through the widespread felling of native pinewoods, but continental birds were successfully reintroduced to Scotland at Taymouth, Perth, in 1837. The first reports of sightings in its erstwhile haunts on the Dee came in around 1878, and in the following year, a hen bird was shot in the wood of Kincorth, Aberdeen. It may have begun to breed near Aberdeen soon afterwards but this remained not proven until 1896, when a nest with six eggs was found in the woodland at Hazlehead. At least one pair continued to nest in the same area in successive years, and a pair is still reported to do so, although this bulky, pugnacious-looking bird is remarkably adept at avoiding the public gaze.

At the time the Caper was colonising Hazlehead, its close relative, the Black Grouse, was evidently disappearing from the same area. It was reported as decreasing in 1916 and no longer breeds near Aberdeen, possibly because of a combination of over-shooting and a reduction in areas of heather-covered ground, although there was a general Scottish decline in the early years of this century.

Hazlehead is one of the few city parks to contain a pond or two. There is nothing very special, admittedly, about the little concrete pool in front of the restaurant, but it does at least contain a limited variety of water beetles and other aquatic life. Its most notable inhabitant is the Mediterranean Bladder-snail, *Physa acuta*. This little mollusc is not native to Britain, but has become established in greenhouse tanks and factory pools where the temperature has been raised by hot water inflows. The snail used to be known from a single place in Britain - a water-lily tank at Kew Gardens - but it turned up in a second place at a cotton mill dam at Bannermill, Aberdeen, in around 1900. This mill dam was filled in shortly afterwards, and, to the grief of the two or three people who could have recognised it, that was thought to be the last of *P. acuta*. It has however since popped up in a large number of places elsewhere, and the Hazlehead snails are most probably the product of an accidental re-intoduction, imported together with the water plants.

Mention Hazlehead to a knowledgeable local botanist, and one plant immediately springs to their mind: *Linnaea*, the Twinflower. Of all the wild flowers of the north east, this one has the most glamour. It is sufficiently elusive to require careful searching, but not so rare as to make the quest a hopeless one, and its twin bells of the palest pink, subtended on wiry stems and mats of neat rounded leaves, are attractive enough to have tempted many a gardener. Linnaeus himself was engagingly modest about his eponymous flower: '*Linnaea*,' he wrote, 'was named by the celebrated Gronovius, and is a plant of Lapland, lowly, insignificant, disregarded, flowering only for a short while - named after Linnaeus who resembles it.' *Linnaea* escaped everyone's attention in Britain until 1795, when Professor James Beattie discovered it in the woods of Inglismaldie, near the North Esk. It was subsequently found in half a dozen places close to Aberdeen, including Hazlehead, but in most of them it no longer survives. Rare flowers do not usually stand up to the advance of suburbia, and if they are not physically obliterated by housing or roads, someone generally digs them up in the end for the rockery.

So far as I can ascertain, *Linnaea* has not been seen under the pines at Hazlehead for some years, but the reason may not necessarily be over-collecting. Another Hazlehead speciality which grew with it was the Ostrich-feather moss, which has been given one of the most resonant of Latin names, *Ptilium crista-castrensis*. The Ostrich-feather moss grows in luxuriant piles of golden-green, which grant it the distinction of being the sole British moss which can be identified at fifty paces. This aristocrat among mosses seems also to have disappeared. It is probable that both plants are victims of a general decline in heathy vegetation at Hazlehead, for they are unlikely to survive long in the thickets or rank grassland which have replaced it. If so, this is also bad news for the last of a trio of Hazlehead rarities, the extraordinary liverwort, *Cryptothallus mirabilis*, which also requires areas of wet, scrubby heather. This odd plant grows entirely underground and was in consequence not noticed in Britain until it was discovered by accident in 1948. Since that date, specialists have taken to excavating holes in suitable areas, and have unearthed *Cryptothallus* in a number of scattered places where it was lurking unseen. To retain any of these three plants at Hazlehead, assuming we have not already lost them, the Council would need to safeguard substantial areas of their habitat.

OTHER GREEN ISLANDS

Although most of Aberdeen's green island are in public ownership, there are a few open spaces which, for one reason or another, have been by-passed and left stranded by the tide of urban growth. One such area whose natural history is comparatively well known is the *Cruikshank Botanic Gardens*, which belongs to the University of Aberdeen. These gardens are surrounded by one of the largest concentrations of professional and student biologists in Britain, and any passing animal would need to be elusive indeed to escape their attention. There is ample evidence to show that the gardens are genuinely rich in wildlife however, and not simply better recorded than similar areas elsewhere. The garden shrubberies provide an abundance of leafy cover for migratory birds, and since the Don migration route lies nearby, and the bushes are not pruned ruthlessly, they have a long and distinguished bird list. Passage birds seeking temporary shelter here include Wood and Garden Warblers, Blackcap, Pied Flycatcher and occasional rarities like Bluethroat. This concentration of small birds must be the reason why this is also one of the best places in the city to see Merlins.

The gardens are notable too for life at a much smaller scale. This is one of the few sites in the country which have a good list of hoverflies, with twenty species (and more undoubtedly awaiting recognition), and although this is partly the consequence of University entomologists strolling through the gardens in their lunch hour, there is, again, more to it than that. There is an abundance of flowers of the right type: flat headed composites like Michaelmas Daisy, spring-flowering shrubs, and ivy blooms on sunny old walls. The sheltered corners and herbaceous borders mask an alien and remorseless world of amazing variety. The larvae of the colourful hoverflies, in particular, are a very mixed crew. The fiercely carnivorous larvae of *Syrphus* snap like terriers among the herds of aphids which form their prey. Lurking in the stagnant pond are the rat-tailed maggots of *Eristalis*, whose telescopic tails pierce the surface film of the water like tiny periscopes. The fat grubs of the large and beautiful fly, *Volucella*, scavenge inside the nests of social wasps (of which there could be up to six species), while hidden away in the soil among the bulbs, are the larvae of the bumble-bee mimic, *Merodon*.

The same pond contains a number of interesting molluscs, which were probably introduced with the water weed. They include those two giants, the Great Pond-snail, whose whorled shell can grow up to two inches long, and the Large Ramshorn, whose shell is coiled in the shape of a Catherine wheel. Both are characteristic of stagnant, weedy pools, and they perform a valuable function by grazing the slimy algal growth which might otherwise choke the pond. The presence of this pond may be one reason why migrating birds congregate here: like a desert oasis, it is one of the few areas where they can quench their thirst.

Rubislaw Den must be one of the city's best known and least visited refuges. A narrow defile of the Denburn, it was far too steep to build on, and was eventually surrounded and virtually sealed off except at the western end, by substantial granite Victorian houses. In the nineteenth century, when Rubislaw Den was more accessible, it was a popular venue for university botanical excursions, and a good haul of plants was always found on its shady banks. The ground flora, like the trees, is a hotch-pot of native and introduced species. Most of the introductions are probably escapes from the gardens above the den. At one time they included Green Hellebore, Cuckoo-pint, Barberry and other plants more reminiscent of the south. Many of these may have disappeared, but one notable survivor, which could be native here, is the Wood Garlic, whose beautiful, stellate flowers belie the uncompromising stink of its broad, shiny leaves. Other local north eastern wild flowers of the den include Smooth-stalked Sedge, Moschatel and the Perforate St Johns-wort. The general vegetation is one of acidic soils, and is dominated by heather, blaeberry and Greater Woodrush.

The den is particularly noted for two birds. One is the Dipper, a country bird which has turned up in a number of British towns and cities recently, wherever the running water is sufficiently clean. The other is the Hawfinch. Aberdeen lies well to the north of the normal breeding range of this burly finch, but it is not a bird given to migratory habits. It has been seen so regularly in the neighbourhood of Rubislaw Den, that there is an outside chance that it actually nests there in small numbers. What attracts the Hawfinch to Aberdeen? There are two possibilities: firstly, that the abundant flowering cherries, which are so much a feature of Victorian Aberdeen, form an attraction for a bird whose 'favourite' food is cherry stones, and that Rubislaw Den is simply the nearest patch of undisturbed tall woodland. The other is that the Hawfinch may be present not only in urban Aberdeen, but in the country as well, and this very elusive bird has simply been overlooked: it is one of the maxims of natural history that one sees what one expects to see; the unexpected is often passed over. During the breeding season, the Hawfinch virtually disappears from view, and the chances of locating a nest are practically nil; otherwise I should hesitate to name its locality.

In many British cities, old graveyards have become excellent refuges for wildlife, and at least one, Highgate Cemetary, is now a nature reserve. The older slabs become richly encrusted with lichens except where the air is polluted, and the natural grassland of rural graveyards has become the last refuge of many a rare flower. This is not the case in Aberdeen, however. Cemetaries like Allenvale are among the most highly maintained plots of ground in the city, and are therefore among the least productive for wildlife. The cult of ancestor worship is alive and well in Aberdeen, and the Forefathers who helped to reclaim the city from the wilderness sleep in comparatively inert surroundings.

The other main wildlife refuge within the city is the industrial sites: the rank growth around disused mills on the Don, the granite quarries which once provided the city with its building blocks, and the Donside sand and gravel quarries. When they have not been infilled and levelled, such places often become reservoirs of young woodland and rank vegetation, like Rubislaw and Persley quarries today. Persley, in particular, is a jumble of dense birch thickets, willowherb beds and patches of more mature woodland with beech, rowan and even oak. Although one would not expect to find anything particularly rare there, such quarries can support quite a diverse flora of colonist 'weeds' and grassland plants, and it is well known that such places often have interesting populations of insects. At least three native flowers, Heath Pearlwort and the Common and Slender Cudweeds seem to be found more often in disused granite quarries than anywhere else. The disused sand quarry at Dyce has been colonised by the only large population of Sand Martins near Aberdeen, and its wet floor is used by a variety of wading birds. The potential of such sites once the quarry ceases to be active, is considerable. Unfortunately the present interest of the Dyce quarry may be a transient phase, a limbo between quarrying and another use. Backfilling for redevelopment has already begun, and there are rumours adrift of marinas and boating pools.

Most of Aberdeen's remaining quarries are comparatively unexplored territory. One reason is inaccessibility: the depths of Rubislaw Quarry would deter a Chris Bonnington. But there can be little doubt that neglected quarries are often repellent places, for waste ground attracts rubbish as naturally as a carcass attracts flies. This is one reason why the city takes care to make its parkland look as tidy as possible. Any piece of rough ground with road access, attracts its quota of rusting cars, rotting mattresses and the immortal type of polythene garbage which resists every attempt by nature's agents to break it down. Holes in the ground are the most attractive dumping ground of all, and they are in considerable demand by the City Cleansing Department. Rubbish dumping is not always so much inimical to wildlife as inimical to naturalists, except perhaps for objects like the pile of herbicide containers which were seen recently at Persley Quarries. The pools which often form on the quarry floor are more susceptible to pollution. The three small ponds in Tyrebagger Quarry, for instance, are heavily enriched with fertilisers and the run-off from refuse dumps, and one at least is covered by a film of oil. This is unfortunate, since such sites are among the few bodies of standing freshwater in the city.

Chapter 5

The Dee and the Don

The Royal Dee, one of the great rivers of Europe, must be among the fairest watercourses to grace a city. It must also be among the very few which are virtually unpolluted from source to mouth, a flow of pure, clear mountain water, even where its banks are lined with houses. The Dee is uniquely important in several other ways. It has the greatest altitudinal range of any major river in Britain, with its source at over four thousand feet, where it bubbles through the Braeriach gravel; it is one of the few large upland river systems to remain unimpeded by reservoirs and hydro-electric dams; and it is one of Britain's best examples of a river consisting entirely of oligotrophic or base-poor waters.

The Dee forms the southern boundary of Aberdeen District from Peterculter to the Brig o' Dee. This is the least pure stretch of the river, but even here the water is only moderately enriched. Until its untimely demise in 1980, the papermill at Peterculter caused an abrupt injection of nutrients into the river via the Culter Burn, but this effect was a transitory one and was soon diluted. Further down, a series of small sewage outlets and the accumulative effect of the run off agricultural fertilisers raises the alkalinity of the water, but, again, not to any significant degree. Since the bulk of the city's sewage is piped out to sea and heavy industry is concentrated well away from the river, the Dee is free from the worst excesses of a large city. In August 1970, the lower reach of the river became slightly discoloured for a while, but the cause of this was traced to plankton blooms in the Loch of Skene and not to any direct man-made cause.

The invertebrate fauna of the Dee is one characteristic of upland rivers and its composition remains more or less the same from top to bottom - an unusual feature in itself. In 1980, a survey of the river by M B Davidson of the University Zoology Department showed that the fauna contains a high proportion of species of well-oxygenated streams, such as stoneflies and mayflies. There is no true lowland reach, and the variety of invertebrates increases only in places where silt has collected or where the river has become slightly enriched, such as at Cults, where sixty seven species were recorded, the highest total anywhere on the river. Of the animals living in and around the Dee, the king is, of course, the Salmon. Salmon has been part of the staple trade of the burgh throughout its history, and Parson Gordon's map of 1661 shows the town's fishing bothies perched on the long, narrow Inch in the midst of the estuary. A line of men are depicted on the shore, holding on to one end of the net like a tug o' war team, while the other is attached to a small boat in midstream. There were frequent squabbles between the riparian owners and the burgh fishers at this time, and once, in 1664, events moved perilously close to a pitched battle. In the heyday of the late eighteenth century, an average of a thousand to twelve hundred barrels of salmon, each weighing four hundredweights, were taken from the Dee, and nearly as many from the Don. The spring run of Salmon used to be the main run on the Dee, but in recent years there has been an alarming tailing off in numbers.

The regular run of eels is sometimes almost as spectacular as those of the Salmon and Sea-trout. The Old Statistical Account records a particularly large run at Aberdeen in May and June of 1793:

> 'The eels kept near the bank and near the surface of the water. They proceeded in regular rows, close to each other, and seven eels in a row ... They continued running three days ... returning from August to October'.

The Dee holds at least one other animal of economic importance: the freshwater Pearl Mussel. Empty mussel shells have been found in the Peterculter and Milltimber area, but they are rarely found much further downstream. Where the mussels occur, they are still fairly common, probably because professional pearl hunters know that the Dee mussels are very poor producers of pearls and do not bother with them. The Don mussels are better pearl- producers, unfortunately for them, and have become rare as a consequence.

The fully aquatic plants of the river are even sparser than the fauna. Few species of higher plants can take root in the rapid current and gravelly substrate of the river bed, and the few that do are generally confined to the quieter stretches. Even at Cults, the most that could be found were two species of moss, and the riverine form of the Bulbous Rush. A few hundred yards further down and the vegetation was confined to a thin scum of blue-green algae and diatoms over the pebbles.

Because the headwaters of the Dee lie in the Cairngorms and the neighbouring mountain glens to the south, seeds or vegetative frag-

Fig. 5. Mown grass and planted trees at the Brig o' Dee.

Fig. 6. River shingle at the Brig o' Dee; one of Aberdeen's most characteristic wild habitats.

ments of arctic-alpine flowers often find their way into the river. These frequently establish on the open, shingly banks of the Dee, many miles from their normal haunts, since these banks can form a good approximation of their wet, rocky mountain habitat. Their toe-hold on the Dee banks and islands is usually temporary, since they are swept away when the Dee is in spate. They have occurred at one time or another along almost the entire river as far as the Brig o' Dee in Aberdeen. In the last century, Mountain Sorrel, Mountain Rock-cress and Alpine Willow-herb grew on the pebbly reaches and islands immediately west of the old bridge, whilst other upland and northern species growing in similar places included Globeflower, Spignel, Lady's Mantle, Water Avens, Northern Bedstraw and Tea-leaved Willow. Another group of plants establish themselves from the opposite direction on shingle in the tidal reaches of the river; these include Sea Plantain, Buckshorn Plantain, Scurvy Grass, Sea Campion and Thrift, which are usually thought of as plants of coastal cliffs.

The abundance of wild flowers along some of the natural banks of the Dee could scarcely form a stronger contrast with the lack of vegetation in the river itself. Some of the best river shingles of the lower Dee are the islands. *Cults Island*, at only thirty feet or so above sea level, is a classic locality for arctic-alpine flowers, which now occur here at their lowest point on the river. The open gravel and shingle which is necessary for the establishment of these plants is to some extent preserved at Cults by the 'Shakkin' Briggie', whose stanchions have blocked the flow of river debris and caused it to accumulate. Since most of the island lies within the flood zone of the river, and, moreover, is within the tidal reach, it provides an ideal catchment area for seeds and propagules from both upstream and from the coast. The shingles are also the home of various garden escapes, of which the most conspicuous is the large Middle Eastern bellflower, *Campanula lactiflora*. The south bank of the river is also an interesting area which has changed remarkably little in the past century or more. In the excellent ash, alder and willow woods of the banks between Cults and Maryculter, one can still find, as MacGillivray did over 130 years ago, blooms such as Moschatel and Water Pepper.

Kincausie Island, two miles upriver from Cults, is a larger and equally interesting island but one of a different character. Here the shingle has long stabilised, and much of the island is covered by alder and willow trees; indeed this is one of the best and least disturbed alder woods in the entire Dee valley. The profusion of lupins on the Kingcausie Island is a celebrated local feature. The inflow stream of the south bank, with its woods and rocky defiles is of considerable botanical interest, and this area was once a popular haunt for excursionists from Aberdeen. An interesting and quite large patch (twenty five acres) of natural river floodplain survives at Pitfodel's Castle. This diamond-shaped area was probably an island until fairly recently, and it is still surrounded by water on three sides. The northern bank holds a scrub of willow, alder and Grey Poplar, much of which is sometimes flooded. There are small reedbeds nearby. To the south, the drier ground rises above the water table, and birch scrub and tall grassland have established. The present river bank is lined by a mixture of trees including oak and Scots Pine. Despite the presence of exotics, like Snowberry and Himalayan Balsam, this is one of the wildest areas in Aberdeen City, and demonstrates an interesting range of natural successions from reedbed to woodland.

The present flora of the Dee banks is a curious mixture of native and introduced wild flowers. The indigenous species were joined by the Monkeyflower introduced from America in about 1820, the Himalayan Balsam in the past fifty years, and the Japanese Knot-grass which, Trail observed, had appeared 'not unlikely to establish itself' in 1920, and is now spreading with a greater rapidity than most would wish. Even Sweet Cicely, that charming, feathery umbellifer whose crushed leaves smell deliciously of aniseed, is thought to be an introduction, and was evidently much less common in 1860 than it is today.

The best known introduction of all must be the Blue Lupin which has become so much a part of the scenery of the Dee that it is difficult to imagine the river without it. The lupin of the Dee is a native of the north west Pacific coast of America, and its specific name, *nootkatensis*, is derived from the Nootka Indians of Vancouver Island. It is a quite separate species from its multicoloured fellow American, the Garden Lupin. There is a conflict in evidence as to when and how the Blue Lupin became established on the Dee. Trail, who was particularly interested in the plant, wrote:

> 'I have been informed that when Balmoral was purchased for Queen Victoria in 1847, this lupine was among the earlier plants brought to the garden of the castle, and that from there its seeds were carried down the Dee, lodging on shingle along its course and gradually extending along its bed.'

The earliest recorded sighting known to him was from Aboyne in 1862, but it had evidently been known from the woods at Balmoral for many years before that. According to Trail, it was rare below Banchory until 1870, but in the following years it spread rapidly downriver, culminating in a fine display on the shingle island opposite Banchory House, on the very outskirts of Aberdeen. Trail's testimony is strengthened by the absence of any mention of the lupin in Dickie's Flora, written in 1860. It would seem, therefore, that its establishment can be dated with unusual accuracy, but MacGillivray's *Natural History of Deeside* (1855) casts this neat story into confusion. For he states that the Blue Lupin was 'common' on the lower Dee, at least ten years before Trail's first observation. Perhaps the solution to the mystery is that Trail spent his boyhood in Orkney, and began attending school in Aberdeen only in 1862, the year he found the 'first' lupin.

The Balmoral connection seems quite feasible, however. The Pacific coast of North America was a favourite haunt of botanical explorers in the early nineteenth century, and among them were Scots, such as David Douglas, of Douglas Fir fame. They were the first Europeans to see the beautiful blue drift of wild lupin, growing in a setting and climate so evocative of Scotland. When specimens were returned to Britain, who would be more likely to receive them and plant them out in the Dee valley than Queen Victoria? Balmoral cannot be the only source of the lupin though, since it is equally well established on the shingles of the Spey and the Tay.

The spread of the Blue Lupin did not please everyone. Despite his fascination for the plant, Trail noted that wherever it established, it quickly crowded out the delicate mountain plants of the river banks, and furthermore raised the beds of shingle above the normal flood-line of the river. Without this periodic scouring action by the current, coarse grasses could take root and then take over, and the open conditions necessary for many of the rarer flowers often disappeared. This may be one reason why the high mountain plants seem to be less common on the river now than they were a century ago. On the other hand, there are equally many places where the lupins and the native flora seemingly co-exist without undue competition, and the presence of the lupin is often a good guide to the most botanically interesting places. A more recent introduction, Japanese Knot-grass, whose broad leaves and bushy habit eventually eliminate all other vegetation, is potentially much more damaging to the native flora.

The natural bank vegetation of the Dee retreated steadily westwards as the city expanded. The canalisation of the river with artificial stone banks and tree-lined esplanades, resulted in the loss of most of the more interesting plants below the Brig o' Dee. The south bank of the Dee is less altered from its original condition than the north, and willow, alder and hazel bushes have been planted in this area, in the heart of the city. The steep, inaccessible bank near the railway bridge still bears a fragment of woodland, much as it did in 1850. A few wild flowers are almost confined to the urban part of the Dee. One of these is Creeping Yellow-cress, a lowland riverbank species which becomes increasingly rare in the north of Britain. Its original home was on one of the Inches in the Dee estuary, and it may have been introduced in imported ballast, during the construction of the docks. Another rare lowlander is Gipsy-wort, a robust, shaggy-leaved marsh plant which occurs on one of the river islands.

The birds of fast, clear water - the Dipper, Grey Wagtail and Common Sandpiper - are more or less frequently seen on the Dee except in the very lowest reaches of the river, and Goosander sometimes sit about on the bars of shingle in the city during the spring and autumn. In very severe winters, the lower Dee becomes an important area for wintering duck such as Goldeneye. In general, however, the Aberdonian Dee is less attractive to the birdwatcher than the Don, although there are a few places of exceptional interest. One such area lies below the Dee Motel, where the river bank vegetation is still rough and willow bushes provide cover for small birds. Beech trees have been planted along the upper part of the bank, apparently in order to prevent the lights of the Motel from shining onto the surface of the water and frightening the fish! This small area contains good numbers of breeding Reed Bunting, Willow Warbler, Sedge Warbler and Whitethroat, as well as one of the two main Pied Wagtail summer roosts in Aberdeen. Unfortunately no rough ground in modern Aberdeen is safe; a sewage outlet nearby this site is probably harmless, but the willows are said to be threatened by the axe, and if they are all removed, this section of bank will lose most of its ornithological interest. That so many small birds should congregate in this rather ordinary spot, suggest that there are very few other suitable places where they can roost and breed on the river, down-stream of Garthdee.

THE DON

To the naturalist, the Aberdonian Don has one clear advantage over the Dee. It has steep, wooded banks which have in many places re-mained wild and undisturbed. They form a green, leafy enclave through the heart of the old industrial zone of the city, and have been described as 'probably unique in the country as an example of *rus in urbe*.'[1] The Don itself is a river of entirely different character to the Dee. Its catchment is mostly agricultural land and, for much of its course, the Don is a slow moving, silty river, and its waters are much richer in dissolved minerals than the Dee. The difference between them is summed up in that well known couplet,

1   Alexander Keith, A Thousand Years of Aberdeen.

'ae mile o' Don's worth twa o' Dee
Except for salmon, stane and tree'.

Let us first take a look at the river itself. Above Inverurie, the Don is almost as clean and pure as the Dee, winding slowly through the fields and forests of a depopulated countryside. The river absorbs the wastes of Inverurie without radical change to the quality of its water, but once it crosses the Aberdeen District boundary at Parkhill, a sudden and drastic change takes place. Between Parkhill and Seaton, the gradient of the river suddenly steepens, increasing the velocity of the current, as it tumbles over a long series of weirs. It was for this reason that early textile and paper industries, which were based on water power, were attracted to the Don rather than the Dee which, in its lower reaches at least, is the slower the two. The large paper mill at Stoneywood was established as long ago as 1771, and the river no doubt received its first dose of pollution at that time. Certainly the lower Don has been badly polluted for as long as anyone can remember and no one has serious doubts as to the cause. At Stoneywood and again at Bucksburn large modern papermills discharge their various noxious wastes and by-products directly into the river, and these are joined, a little further downstream, by the effluent from the Bucksburn sewage plant. The sewage, my informant tells me, 'is pretty bad at the moment', but although unpleasant to human beings, it has a relatively small effect on the flora and fauna of the river. The principal culprits are the mills, and the really damaging effluents are the organic starches and paper additives which form a rich 'nutrient soup', that is greedily feasted on by that least prepossessing of all living things, sewage fungus.

The sewage fungus of the Don is not a true fungus, but a type of bacteria, *Sphaerotilus natans*. Incubating in the polluted water in early spring, *Sphaerotilus* grows with alarming speed. Under the microscope, it resembles an ever-extending chain of beads, embedded in a sheath of mucilage. The mass effect is to produce a flocculent growth like slimy cotton wool, which carpets the river bed and smothers the nooks and crannies which form the haunts of most of the natural denizens of the river. The sinister appearance of the sewage fungus is enhanced by its bright orange colour. The cause of this startling colouration is shrouded in mystery, but since the paper mills also empty dyes into the river, which have at times been known to turn the water pink or green, it seems probable that dyes have been picked up in the slime of the fungus. In a bad season, the lower Don can be quite a sight: bloated orange masses, carpeting a river of coloured water, with chunks of sewage rolling gently past in the current.

Fig. 7. *Rus in urbe*: the wooded banks of the Don, in the heart of modern Aberdeen.

Fig. 8. The Donmouth sand spit is the last remaining area of natural blown sand between the Don and the Dee.

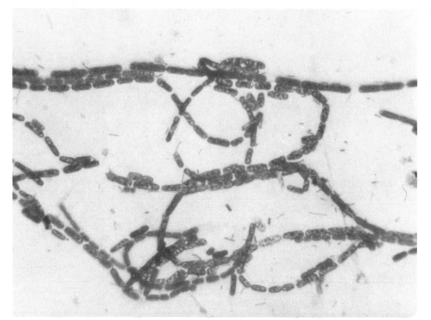

Fig. 9. Sewage Fungus (*Sphaerotilus natans*) under a high power light microscope during its early stages of growth.

Fig. 10. A rare photograph of Dickie's Bladder-fern, *Cystopteris dickieana*.

Surprisingly enough, there is still life lurking among the slime, which makes up in quantity what it lacks in diversity. The fungus supports a food-web of organisms which live among its growth like animals in a forest. When the sewage fungus is at its peak, the water becomes starved of dissolved oxygen, and hence there are no fish, few molluscs and none of the inhabitants of cleaner water. Life in a polluted river tends to be worm-like or microscopic, but such organisms have their own fascination. Activated sewage sludge can become an object of strange beauty when sufficiently magnified, with tiny but exotic animalcules sporting about their chosen domain like tropical fish around a coral reef. The first signs of life in the sewage fungus forest are different types of bacteria, and it is their presence which renders the water unsafe to drink. Soon they are joined - and eaten - by more complex single-celled animalcules, including those old school favourites, *Amoeba* and *Paramecium*. One form, *Carchesium*, is large enough to be visible to the naked eye, and under a lens becomes a beautiful object of divided stalks crowned with ciliated bells, as delicate and graceful as a branched coral. The next stage in the food-web is provided by seething masses of worm-like animals, which include Oligochaetes, the true worms, leeches and blood-red Chironomid midge larvae stuck into the mud head first inside a tube, with their tails wagging above in the slow current. Few of these are known to feed directly on the sewage fungus, which seems to be virtually immune from attack, although the Enchytraeids or pot-worms are suspected of doing so. One particular worm of the lower Don deserves special mention. This is the large splendid leech, *Trocheta bykowskii*, which can grow up to eight inches long when extended, and is said to be so hideous in appearance, that hardened freshwater scientists have been known to recoil in horror on seeing it for the first time. *Trocheta* is quite harmless to human beings and spends most of its life among the ooze, devouring small worms and midge larvae whole. Its most remarkable characteristic is its amphibious habits, for it readily takes to the land where it preys on slugs, and burrows into the soil and decaying vegetation near the water edge. Its close and equally large relative, *T. subviridis*, sometimes enters sewers and drains, and has shown a distressing tendency to turn up unexpectedly in lavatories and sinks!

So long as one keeps aesthetics firmly out of the argument, there is a world of wonder in a polluted river like the lower Don. But it is a grotesque and perverted parody of nature. Moreover, the sewage fungus has an unpleasant way of drawing attention to itself: the infamous Don Pong. When the fungus has completed its annual growth, clumps are detached by the current and swept downriver to the shallow water of the estuary. Here, slumped in heaps like loathsome fleeces, it is slowly decomposed by the sulphate-reducing bacteria which occur naturally in the estuarine mud. The by-product of this process is that gas of rotten eggs, hydrogen sulphide, which is the progenitor of the Don Pong. The Pong has been lying low in recent years, apart from a resurgence in the drought of 1976, which sent local journalists scurrying to their typewriters. The absence of the Pong, and the more moderate quantities of the fungus recently, have given rise to the popular myth that the Don is becoming cleaner. Sad to say, this does not appear to be the case, although it is probably true that it is less polluted now than, say, forty years ago. What has happened in recent years is that a succession of wet summers have increased the flow rate of the river, which has in turn impeded the growth of the fungus. The fungus is also showing an odd and so far unexplained seasonal distribution, with a single 'burst' in the spring and early summer at Seaton Park, but two bursts in spring and autumn further upriver. The overall level of pollution has in fact remained essentially the same over the period, since 1975, in which the North East River Purification Board have monitored the river. Seven years of 'discussions' have not yet persuaded the guilty parties to moderate their rate of discharge into the river. Until they do, the Don Pong problem is shelved rather than solved, and another warm, dry summer should bring about its return. What I personally find most intriguing about all this is that the Don water has evidently never been tested to see whether or not it is a public health danger. Since the Aberdeen stretch is used as a slalom course by canoeists one might regard such an investigation as, to say the least, relevant.

Despite the polluted water, Salmon and Sea-trout usually manage to penetrate the lower reaches of the Don on their way to their spawning grounds, since the rapid current ensures a sufficiency of dissolved oxygen in the water. Occasionally there are fish kills, the last serious one being in 1971, when dozens of dead salmon were recovered. Another hazard they face are would-be salmon poachers, who sometimes use the protective wire-netting aroung the sapling trees in Seaton Park as ready made fish traps. Few resident fish can survive in the lower Don, however, except perhaps for the Three-spined Stickleback whose tolerances are astonishingly wide. Above the polluted stretch, the river contains Pike, Minnows and the northernmost population of Gudgeon in Britain. The Gudgeon is almost certainly an escape: they used to be used by fishermen as live-bait when spinning for salmon. A bait-can full of Gudgeon upset either accidentally or deliberately into the river in around 1900, probably explains their presence there today.

The Don has a richer aquatic flora than the Dee and the silty sediments of the quieter stretches are favoured by a variety of flowering plants. In the neighbourhood of Seaton Park, river plants include a Water Crowfoot (opinions differ as to which one it is), Water Milfoil, Branched Bur-reed and at least four species of Pondweed. A fifth Pondweed, an uncommon hybrid rejoicing in the name of *Potamogeton x sparganifolius*, forms extensive patches on rocks in the fast reaches of the river near Dyce. Once one emerges onto the banks, however, most of the characteristic species found by the Dee are missing: no mountain plants, since the Don catchment excludes high mountains; no lupins and shingle plants for there is no extensive river shingle. Instead, we find a good variety of common lowland plants of riversides, marshes and woods, with a smattering of more local species.

The spectacular spread of the lupin on the Dee is paralleled in less spectacular fashion admittedly, by the spread of the Reed Sweet Grass on the Don. The first north eastern record of this tall grass, which is often mistaken for the true Reed, was from a pond at Breda in the Howe of Alford, in 1836. This pond lies less than half a mile from the Don and is separated from it by a flat stretch of marshy ground. By 1860, the grass had 'escaped' and become naturalised by the Don, several miles downriver of its original location. By 1880, it had spread as far as Persley, where it 'formed beds of tall stems and leaves, making in many places a continuous belt along the shores and crushing out and killing the native herbage of the banks'.[1] By 1920, the Reed Sweet Grass had conquered the Don, having spread right down to the lifeboat house near the river mouth. It remains a common Donside grass.

The wilder banks of the Don, like those of the Dee, contains a curious mixture of native and introduced species, and in many cases it would be impossible to tell the difference without foreknowledge. Thus long-established introductions like Dame's Violet, Monkeyflower, White Butterbur and Leopard's Bane rub shoulders with the native flowers and, to my eyes at least, enhance rather then detract from the interest of the bankside vegetation. So far as I am aware, no one has yet explained the unusual success by which so many escapes have established themselves in the north east. Perhaps it is because there are vacant 'niches' in the wild, due to an impoverished indigenous flora. If so, it is odd that such an aggressive Triffid of a plant as Giant Hogweed has not been the runaway success on the Don that it is on the Findhorn and many other eastern rivers.

The trees of the lower Don valley are among the most valuable of the city's wildlife resources. In places it is easy to forget that one is not only near a city, but, strictly speaking, *in* one, since the Don below

1   Trail, Flora of Aberdeen.

Persley is more or less surrounded by houses, tower blocks and mills. The illusion is greatly strengthened on the not infrequent occasions when one spies a Buzzard, Heron or Roe Deer. These woods, like the bankside flowers, are a mixture of the natural and the exotic. One of the City's three Nature Trails runs along the southern side of the Don, between Grandholme and Persley Bridges and, in less than a mile, one passes by native oak, ash, holly and Wych elm, naturally regenerating introductions like beech and sycamore, planted utilitarian trees like hornbeam, maple, walnut and White Willow, and exotic follies like Monkey Puzzle. Perhaps the most interesting single tree on the walk is a lonely Almond Willow, no longer a fine upstanding tree, but, in the words of the trail booklet, an 'old stump ... still with growth on it'. This is a rare willow in Scotland and is probably of planted origin. An apparent hybrid between the Almond and White Willow also occurs quite commonly along the Culter Burn near Peterculter. The authorities have left much of the Donside woodland as they found it, but their restraint in this area is replaced by wholehearted exuberance when one passes down river to the river banks and island at Seaton Park: 'We planted a whole mixture of things'. This extraordinary area would keep a trained botanist busy for hours; the mixture includes, for some reason best known to those that planted them, an unusually high percentage of poisonous shrubs such as Laburnum and Alder Buckthorn.

The woodland at Gordon Mills and Bridge of Don is of more natural appearance. Although planted beech occupies most of the accessible south bank, there is woodland on the northern banks whose composition is close to what would have been there originally: oak, ash, and Wych elm, although a discordant element is added by the abundance of sycamore. This is one of those places which provide a banquet of good things: it is one of the city's wildlife Meccas; lovers of venerable and beautiful objects have the nearby thirteenth century Brig o' Balgownie, and those of romantic bent may allow themselves to feel a scintillation of terror, as Byron did, from the evil river kelpies of Black Nook Pot, the dark hole in the river below the bridge. Even geologists are provided with something to interest them: the small rock outcrops immediately downstream of the bridge are said to be of national importance. They are, in the jovial language of science, 'basal conglomerates of Old Red Sandstone, resting unconformably on the edges of Dalradian schists.' In everyday parlance, this is something which is unusual and it provides specialists with food for thought and debate.

The woodland flora of the Don banks is predominantly that of poor soils, and consisting in the main of rather dull grassland. On the steeper, shadier and less accessible slopes there are a number of plants which are almost unknown elsewhere in the city. Near the Brig o' Balgownie grow a pair of garlics, the broad-leaved Wood Garlic or Ransoms and the chive-like growth of Crow Garlic, which seldom condescends to flower, but has successfully spread there by its proliferation of vegetative bulbils. Another notable flower of this area is the Intermediate Enchanter's Nightshade, a hybrid which seems to have gradually taken over the places formerly occupied by one of its parents, the Alpine Enchanter's Nightshade. Upstream, between the Brig o' Balgownie and Grandholme Bridge, there were, formerly at least, the only locations near Aberdeen for Wood Goldilocks, Marsh Yellow-cress, and Wood Club-rush. The botanical prize, however, should perhaps go to the Bluebells of Balgownie. These are said to be genuine wild hyacinth which is far more rarely seen in the north east than the grosser hybrids and Spanish varieties which escape from gardens.

The Don woods are important refuges for birds and mammals. Perhaps the single most important locality is the wooded island downstream of the Brig o' Balgownie which, in contrast with the island at Seaton, has been left in a natural condition. Its dense thickets of willow-herb provide a roosting site for three hundred or more Teal and a large summer roost of Pied Wagtails, as well as breeding Mallard and Moorhen. This is also the one place in the city where one might, with luck, espy a Water Rail. A pair of Mute Swans attempt to breed here annually, although their eggs are usually stolen by vandals. This island is remarkably undisturbed, despite the nearby traffic roaring past over the Bridge of Don. It also lies in an area of shallow, relatively still water, and both factors contribute towards its excellence as a locality for birds. Between the island and the Brig o' Balgownie lies the Black Nook Pot, a good place to see Goldeneye, Goosander, Teal, Little Grebe and other wildfowl. Almost every species of bird which nests near Aberdeen has been seen by the Don banks at one time or another. They are particularly good places to see or, more often hear, summer visitors such as Blackcap, Chiffchaff and Black Redstart, and they contain a greater density of the commoner warblers, finches and thrushes than most other parts of the city. The most conspicuous avian spectacle is the huge rookery between the Brig o' Balgownie and Gordon Mills, a reminder that north east Scotland has some of the largest rookeries in Britain, and this one is surely the largest in any city.

The mammals of the Don are much more elusive and less well known. There are probably more small mammals here than anywhere else in the city and it is a particularly important foraging area for bats. Dr Paul Racey has found a remarkable correlation between wooded river courses and the presence of bats in the north east. On the banks of the

Don near Seaton Park they are often seen foraging around the tree tops and over the slow reaches of the river. Although it is difficult to identify bats in flight, the majority of those seen on the Don are likely to be Pipistrelles, whose main food source are the mayflies and midges which occur in large swarms along the banks in the summer months.

Little is known about the status of the larger mammals. Foxes are occasionally glimpsed on the Don banks and the Links. They do not seem to have yet acquired the suburban, dustbin-raiding habits of the foxes of London and other cities, and remain very much animals of open ground. The mink has become established by the Don in the past decade or so, and will probably resist all attempts to get rid of it. There is some doubt whether or not it has a serious effect on the breeding and roosting wildfowl: if the rather unsatisfactory evidence for the mink's unsavoury image as a ravaging killer were presented to an unbiased Scottish jury, the verdict would probably be 'not proven'. Few landowners are prepared to give it the benefit of the doubt. The otter is seldom met with and a question mark must be attached to its status around Aberdeen. Recent reliable sightings include one on the Bridge of Don island in 1971, and this would be perhaps the most likely regular haunt at Aberdeen. A brief note in the Working Mens Natural History Society Transactions of 1916 refers to a pair of otters which were evidently successful at rearing young near the Stoneywood Burn, 'despite attempts to kill them'. The most recent sighting that I know of, was of a single animal crouched on the muddy banks of the Dee, immediately below the harsh walls of Craiginches prison!

OTHER URBAN WATERCOURSES

There are at least twenty five streams within the city of Aberdeen, most of which eventually drain into the Don or the Dee. The North East River Purification Board has begun to monitor the pollution levels of a sample of them, and early results suggest that about half are polluted, and the others are in reasonable condition. One of the largest watercourses, the Denburn, is surprisingly clean, and contains stoneflies, one of the most pollution-sensitive groups, in the parts of central Aberdeen, such as Rubislaw Den and Cherryvale, where the stream still follows its natural channel. At the other extreme is Far Burn, the main stream draining Dyce Airport, whose fauna has been unappetisingly described as 'a mass of wriggling worms'.

Chapter 6

Wilderness in Bondage

In this and the following chapter, we pass out of the city into the rural landscape of Aberdeen District. Three quarters of the total area of the District can still be described as countryside, although it is countryside dominated by the town. Large areas of farmland in the former parishes of Nigg and Old Machar have been developed into industrial and residential estates, sometimes leaving patches of open country stranded precariously as 'open spaces' amid the new housing. Much of the remaining countryside is protected by green belt policies, and a considerable acreage is publicly owned for the benefit of the townsman, with outdoor recreation as the principle land-use. Thus Hazlehead and Brimmond Hill to the west and Loirston to the south are Country Parks, and other open spaces to the north of Aberdeen are, or have been, on the drawing board for similar status. Further to the west, the Forestry Commission is the largest landowner, and its extensive plantations at Kirkhill and Countesswells are partly open to the public and equipped with car parks and forest trails.

The remaining traditional countryside of Aberdeen District was moulded in the era of farming improvements in the late eighteenth century. It is a landscape of square, stone-dyked fields, interspersed with shelter belts and plantations and intersected by a maze of narrow lanes. On Deeside there are numerous baronial mansion houses, once the homes of prosperous merchants, but which are now often decaying or being converted into hotels. Apart from the dwindling patches of bog, valley woodland and heath, this is a relatively recent man-made landscape, and there are none of the ancient managed woodlands or old pastures which are still a prominent feature of the lowland countryside further south. And what fragments of past landscapes remain near Aberdeen are there for a specific purpose. Even the austere slopes of Brimmond and Elrick Hills have been domesticated with car parks, recreation furniture and guide books to 'fairy-like dells' and other rustic charms. The wilderness has been tamed.

AGRICULTURAL LAND IN ABERDEEN DISTRICT

Aberdeen is traditionally arable and cattle country, and its farming landscape is a mixture of crop fields and grass. Farming methods have changed considerably over the years, and particularly since 1939, and the ever increasing tendency towards intensification has taken a severe toll of the wildlife which once throve on farmland. It is not the intention to describe in any detail the farming practices of Aberdeen, since this is a book about the urban rather than rural environment. Let us instead take a brief look at some of the characteristic animals and plants of Aberdeen's agricultural land, and see how their numbers have changed in response to changing farming methods.

One of the most vivid indicators of changing conditions in arable land is the Corn Cockle, an attractive bristly weed with large pink flowers, which was once common among cereal crops. We know that Corn Cockle was present at Aberdeen at least as early as the fourteenth century, since its seeds have been found by archaeologists among husks of wheat in a medieval midden. They had evidently been ingested in a wheat loaf by some luckless person, who no doubt suffered mild gastroenteritis, since Cockle seeds are poisonous in quantity. For a long time, the Cockle, like other agricultural weeds, would have been confined to the immediate neighbourhood of Aberdeen; its fortunes were fixed to those of wheat, but after the improvements, there followed at least a century when it was common and familiar wild flower, enjoyed by the wayfarer and loathed by the farmer. The authors of the early floras all agree that it was an everyday plant, and as late as 1860, Dickie could describe it as 'frequent in cultivated fields throughout the district'. The Cockle was an annual and in the north east, its appearance depended on fresh introductions of seed, sown with each crop. It became much less common quite suddenly, once wheat ceased to be grown locally, although it still popped up occasionally among crops of tares. By 1920, Trail regarded it as 'one of the rarer weeds of cultivation around Aberdeen'. In fact, Trail may have been among the last people to see an Aberdonian Cockle growing wild in its 'natural' habitat, a field of corn although Professor Wynne-Edwards found one in flower on a section of recently 'filled' ground between the Esplanade and the Don estuary in 1955. New seed-cleansing techniques introduced in the 1920s eliminated all the Cockle seeds before sowing, and since the plant was unable to support itself independently, it rapidly died out. The Corn Cockle is now one of Britain's most endangered plants: the use of modern herbicides has more or less finished it off, and almost the only place where it can still be found in quantity is on a Cambridgeshire farm, where the owner deliberately practices bad husbandry to preserve it.

Several other local cornfield weeds have suffered a rise and fall scarcely less meteoric. The handsome Greater Hay-rattle, for example, which has now joined the Corn Cockle in the Red Data Book of endangered plants, was unknown in the north east until a single plant appeared in a field of barley, twenty miles north of Aberdeen, in 1894. In subsequent years, it turned up in more and more places; it flourished in a rye-grass field at Grandholme in 1896, and it appeared unexpectedly in odd corners like rubbish tips and stackyards. It was probably introduced among cereal and grass seeds from other parts of Scotland, and found Aberdeen's soil and climate to its liking for, Trail wrote, 'it appears likely to become here, as elsewhere, a troublesome weed ... in fields of oats, barley and grass'. It never did, however. Seed cleansing spelt doom for the Greater Hay-rattle as it did for the Corn Cockle, and yesterday's 'troublesome weed' has become today's cherished rarity.

Other weeds which were formerly common but are rarely seen in crop fields today, include Corn Chamomile, Cornflower, Field Woundwort, Field Penny Cress, Intermediate Dead Nettle and, best known of all, the poppy. The Aberdonian poppies were the type with a long, smooth capsule, *Papaver dubium*, and although once frequent, they were rarely, if ever, common enough to reduce the reaper to slumber, as they did, in the sunny south:

> 'Drows'd with the fume of poppies, while thy hook
> Spares the next swath and all its twined flowers'.

One is much more likely to find poppies in the rather less charming surroundings of refuse tips and old quarries today, where the native red varieties are mixed up with the foreign Opium Poppy.

Some crop weeds remain abundant despite the intensification of farming and the use of herbicides and chemical fertilisers. Potato fields near Aberdeen are sometimes coloured a glorious golden yellow in late autumn by the Corn Marigold, one of a minority of crop weeds which prefers acidic soils. The colourful Large-flowered Hemp-nettle is as common in the north east as anywhere in Britain, and other abundant survivors of the 'Green Revolution' and Common Market subsidies include Common Hemp-nettle, Corn Spurrey, Field Bugloss, Black Bindweed, Lesser Nettle and the immortal Charlock.

Birds have, in general, adapted more successfully to changing farming methods than wild flowers. The only common species known to have suffered a spectacular decline is the Corncrake, which used to be 'plentifully distributed' near Aberdeen in 1900, but, which, as in most other lowland areas on the British mainland, has almost ceased to breed. Their decline is attributed to mechanisation and the cutting of hay meadows, the Corncrake's favoured habitat, before its chicks are fledged. In Dublin and some other Irish cities, the Corncrake has taken to nesting on waste ground near suburban factories, but this habit has not yet caught on in Scotland.

The agricultural expansion around Aberdeen was the probable reason for the population explosion of the Starling in the nineteenth century. It is so familiar a bird today that it is difficult to imagine that prior to 1860, it was a not very common, non-breeding migrant. The increase of improved pasture and arable land provided the Starling with a greatly increased food supply, although it has been suggested that climatic amelioration and the decrease of birds of prey were also factors in its spread. Today the Starling is more abundant than many might wish. The roofs of Mitchell Tower and Marischal College sparkle with the droppings of huge autumnal and winter 'murmerations' of Starlings, and their roosts in deciduous trees, for instance near Burnside Gardens, can be almost deafening.

The Rook, on the other hand, was probably always common (it has been netted and shot in Scotland for at least five and a half centuries), but the agricultural improvement must have greatly increased its available food supply, as a provider of almost limitless seed corn, earth worms and leather-jackets. There are certainly more rookeries in Aberdeen City today than there were during a census of 1900. The Crow has probably also increased its numbers, in a less spectacular way, and its racial characteristics have slowly changed over the past century or more. In 1850, the grey and black Hooded Crow was much more common than the all-black Carrion Crow, although both varieties were present. Since then, the Carrion Crow has replaced the Hooded, and the latter is now comparatively rare.

Between 1972 and 1974, Aberdeen University Bird Club ran an annual Common Bird Census on a fairly typical lowland farm at Loirston, two miles south of the city. This is an area of mixed farming, about half being under oats, barley and hay and the remainder under permanent grass. The field boundaries were traditional drystane dykes, and the available nesting cover was limited to a bank of gorse, and small areas of scrub and woodland. The census area, which covered two hundred and ninety acres, included several small gardens and the open water of Loirston Loch, with its fringing reedbeds. The results of the census, from which I have omitted the nesting wildfowl, were as follows:

Number of breeding pairs

	1972	1973	1974
Skylark	19	28	25
Lapwing	20	9	13
Reed Bunting	15	11	9
Blackbird	14	9	9
Dunnock	11	8	6
Meadow Pipit	11	7	5
Linnet	11	5	11
Corn Bunting	9	7	7
Yellowhammer	5	8	7
Crow	5	3	2
Oystercatcher	4	5	9
Common Gull	4	8	present
Starling	4	4	2
Swallow	3	4	4
Wren	3	3	1
Song Thrush	3	2	1
Sedge Warbler	4	0	0
Pied Wagtail	2	2	3
Curlew	2	2	1
Whitethroat	1	1	2
Chaffinch	present	3	1
Willow Warbler	present	2	1
Magpie	1	2	1
Pheasant	present	2	0
Robin	present	2	present
Kestrel	1	1	present
Redshank	0	present	2
Greenfinch	1	1	present
Snipe			

Common Sandpiper, Jackdaw, Blue Tit, Wheatear, Stonechat and Grey Wagtail were recorded as breeding once only.

Total numbers of nesting pairs	165	160	131
Number of breeding species	28	35	25
Total numbers of species seen	36	46	35

The overall density of around 1.7 to 1.9 acres per pair of breeding birds is well below the national average for farmland. The Census organiser suggests that this is due to the lack of suitable cover, such as hedgerows and woodland with undergrowth. This would explain the low numbers of species which are normally common on farmland, such as Chaffinches, Wrens, Blue Tits, Thrushes and Robins. The only birds which do comparatively well are the ground nesters (which are often vulnerable to grazing livestock) and those which utilise the reed-beds and gorse scrub.

CONIFER PLANTATIONS IN ABERDEEN DISTRICT

Most of Aberdeen's woodlands are conifer plantations and the majority are in the ownership of the Forestry Commission. The biggest of these is *Kirkhill Forest*, a single huge block of trees which occupies 1172 hectares of the undulating upland between the Brimmond and Elrick Country Park and the Don. Further south is a more fragmented area of forest, also owned by the Forestry Commission, in the neighbourhood of Countesswells.

Kirkhill, which is regarded by some as the finest urban forest in Scotland, was utterly treeless in the eighteenth century. Tyrebagger Hill and the Hill of Marcus, which lie within the present day forest were the northernmost of a series of rounded flat-topped ridges between the Don and the Dee, which reached their highest point at Brimmond Hill. Bare, bleak, 'covered with short heath and scattered bushes of broom and furze'[1] and studded with treacherous bogs with names like 'Moss of Rotten', they formed a scene of utter desolation. An old rhyme has it that,

> 'Round Brimmond back and up to Skene
> Wis ae bleak muir o' sax mile wide,
> Wi' scarce a single patch o' green'.

The great impetus towards putting the land into productive use, which followed the new farming methods of the mid-eighteenth century, at first made little impact on this formidable area. The soils at Kirkhill were the poorest in the District, useless for agriculture, and the seaward slopes and tops were exposed to severe salt-laden easterly winds which made afforestation difficult. By 1795, however, the owners had planted three plantations of 'fir', probably Scots Pine, at Tyrebagger, and a hundred and forty acres on the equally poor, but more sheltered ground at Countesswells.[2] More tree planting followed, and by the mid-nineteenth century, one third of the entire parish of Dyce had been converted to forest, most of it since 1828. The trees were mostly Scots Pine and European Larch although MacGillivray noted that Norway

1   Old Statistical Account.
2   ibid.

Spruce and Silver Fir were also widely planted. They evidently grew reasonably well except at the top of Tyrebagger Hill. At Countesswells, which had been planted with the same species, they did even better, since 'the soil seems most congenial'. [3]

A large part of the present Kirkhill Forest and the smaller woods at Countesswells was in existence by 1900. The Forestry Commission had been established for only two years, when it bought a large block of partially afforested land at Kirkhill in 1921, which became one of the earliest of its plantations in north east Scotland. Their other purchases in the Aberdeen area followed Hitler's war, when the remainder of Kirkhill was acquired in 1945, Kingshill and Countesswells in 1946 and Cults Woods in 1957. The Scots Pine and European Larch, which were the chief constituents of the first plantations, have been superseded by American and Far Eastern trees which grow faster on poor soils. Since the soils of Kirkhill are still peaty and prone to waterlogging, despite up to two centuries of continuous tree cover, the current plantations consist of Hybrid and Japanese Larches (19%), Sitka Spruce (34%), and Lodgepole and Beach Pine (39%). A single percent is devoted to broadleaves, which is divided between five hectares of high grade beech and twenty one of low grade beech, the latter being retained for amenity. The oldest of the beeches were planted in around 1870, and those of the present conifers in about 1925. Although the primary function of these woods is to produce a crop of timber, the Forestry Commission have developed some of them for recreation, by creating a network of footpaths and car parks, and providing facilities for riding and wayfaring.

These woods are large enough to contain a lot of wildlife. Unfortunately, most published accounts about the value of conifer plantations for wildlife tend to get bogged down in polemic and propaganda. Apologists for modern economic forestry methods insist that they are benefitting the land by restoring the forest. If it is put to them that modern forests are radically different from the native variety, they can nonetheless retort that any forest is richer in wildlife than the open ground which it has replaced. I find these arguments rather misleading. Modern conifer plantations support a density of bird life which is between one third and one ninth as great as that of natural forest. The diversity of species is also poorer, particularly for warblers and birds which nest in holes in standing timber, such as woodpeckers. And even this limited fauna is almost impossible to see. The Forestry Commission's planting policy has undoubtedly increased the range and abundance of a few birds which do well in coniferous forest, notably

3   Military map by James Robertson of Edinburgh, 1822, quoted in Forestry Commission report.

the Coal Tit and the Goldcrest. Both are common birds, however, and when their increase is presented to the public as justification for more and more blanket afforestation, as sometimes happens, I, for one, begin to feel a little worried. There are at least a million Coal Tits in Britain and one and a half million Goldcrests. Do people want even *more*? Surely there are already enough to satisfy even the most ardent ornithologist!

Perhaps the two most exciting inhabitants of Kirkhill are the Capercaillie and the Crossbill. Both are evidently scarce and seldom seen; the Caper in particular is said not to take to Lodgepole and other 'new' pines, preferring to stick to the old Scots variety. Kirkhill also contains Roe Deer, which are sometimes seen out on more open ground on nearby Elrick Hill.

An example of the losses and gains resulting from the creation of this type of forest is to examine the predicament of a trio of rare woodland moths which are, or were, found in this area. Two of these, which have for reasons mysterious, been given Teutonic names, The Saxon and Cousin German, have a northern montane distribution in Britain, and Countesswells once represented an eastern extension of their usual haunts. The Saxon depended on scrub willow along stream valleys in the Cults-Blacktop area, and since such conditions have survived in a few places where the streambanks have been left unplanted, it may well still occur there, although there are no recent records. The Cousin German, on the other hand, needs large areas of uneconomic birch scrub, and these have almost entirely been replaced by conifers. It is almost certainly extinct at Countesswells. On the credit side, a very rare micro-moth called *Acleris abietana*, which was not recorded anywhere in Britain until 1965, has since turned up in Kirkhill Forest. The caterpillars of *A. abietana* feed on foreign pines and spruces, and it clearly owes its spread to the cultivation of such trees.

The plant life of a conifer plantation, like the fauna, depends on the age of the canopy. The fenced young plantings soon become a tangle of tall grass and bramble, in which the rodent population explodes, and this in turn attracts raptors such as Hen Harrier. Once the trees are tall enough to cast a heavy shade, most of the plant life disappears, except for a variety of toadstools. A number of flowers of natural Scots Pine forest are sometimes found in older plantations of pine , providing the canopy admits enough light. Three of them, Lesser Wintergreen, Lesser Twayblade and Creeping Ladies Tresses, used to occur under a stand of pine by Queens Road West within the city itself, but they disappeared soon after the trees were felled. The Twinflower grew under pines in at least half a dozen localities within the District, and it still occurs on one patch of rocky ground under planted trees. On the whole, however, Aberdeen's plantations are not very interesting to the botanist. Their worst aspect, apart from the visual one, is their uniformity: the natural pattern and variation of the vegetation, with its intimate response to small physical changes, has mostly been lost. The flora of Aberdeen plantations of Kirkhill and Countesswells is, so far as we know, not very different from similar plantations elsewhere in Scotland.

HEATHLANDS

The fragments of heath and bog in the District of Aberdeen which are still unreclaimed generally represent land which is so poor, exposed or water-logged that no one has attempted to bring it into productive use. By Aberdonian standards of agriculture, that means only the poorest land of all. In some cases such land may have been part of an estate whose owner has deliberately retained rough ground for shooting over. In others, such as Scotstown Moor, ancient common rights have prevented the wholesale enclosure and reclamation of the land. Since even the sourest heath must succumb to the steady spread of residential developments, however, the remaining wild heathlands in Aberdeen District lie mostly along the District's boundary at some distance from the City.

The heaths of the former parish of Aberdeen had all gone by about 1880. Of those which are given prominence in the floras, one of the first to go was a marsh at Broad Hill, a locality for the Royal Fern, which was drained in 1797. Ferryhill Moss, the old burgh's source of peat, had been built over by about 1850, and the last survivor, Stocket Moor, had been carved up for cultivation by 1880. With the loss of these heaths, much of the indigenous flora of Aberdeen parish became extinct. The more notable plants which had disappeared by 1880 include Lesser Marshwort, Lesser Bladderwort, Hairy Stonecrop, Fen Bedstraw, Lesser Butterfly Orchid, Lesser Bur-reed and the Stags-horn, Fir and Lesser Clubmosses. One would need to travel a great many miles from Aberdeen to find some of these today.

The heaths of the outlying parishes of the District have not fared quite so badly. The two most extensive areas of heath are now owned by the City, and have been respectively designated as Loirston Country Park and Brimmond and Elrick Country Park. Their wildlife and local history is described in the Department of Leisure and Recreation's booklets, and Loirston forms one of three fragments of Aberdeen's landscape which I describe in some detail in Chapter Nine. The largest sites are not always the most interesting, and *Brimmond and Elrick* in particular suffer from a lack of good wetland sites, Brimmond, says the Country Park booklet, 'is a barren sort of hill, offering little refuge to the wild flower or the tree'. So it is, horribly barren. A great lump of gneiss, scored with Ice Age meltwater channels and topped, at eight hundred and seventy feet, by BP's communication scanners, its lower slopes consist of little more than acre upon acre of dense whin scrub, whilst the higher ground is a solid cap of heather. The scrub is utilised by nesting Whinchat, Stonechat, Whitethroat and Linnet, and the open heath is the domain of Red Grouse and Meadow Pipit. Patches of birch, pine and beech on the more sheltered ground below the south-facing slopes, help to relieve the monotony a little. Dickie recorded Alpine Clubmoss from the summit of Brimmond but this is the only botanical record of note. Most naturalists have found it a dull, bleak hill, and only geologists have much to say in its favour.

The tiny *Den of Maidencraig*, which nestles beneath the A944 near Hazlehead is the opposite end of the scale to Brimmond Hill, but is much more interesting. Formerly open heathland, the den is now a wooded valley of six acres or so, divided into two by a rock buttress and waterfall. At least eleven species of broad-leaved tree are present, including an abundance of hazel, whilst the remaining open ground is covered by heather, blaeberry and woodrush. This used to be a favourite stamping ground of Aberdeen naturalists, who knew it as the nearest locality where Bearberry could be found, as well as other notable plants more common inland, such as Intermediate Wintergreen, Oak Fern and Small White Orchid. The den is also a noted locality for mosses and fungi, and an unusual variety of the large woodland moths known as 'the Prominents' have been taken here. One recent arrival which the earlier naturalists would not have been familiar with is the stupendous Giant Hogweed, that sinister and alien invader of our river sides. The Den of Maidencraig is still surprisingly unspoiled, although a tractor path has recently been driven through to the waterfall from the western end.

The largest tract of wet moorland within the District is *Leuchar Moss*, at Garlogie. Leuchar Moss is *very* wet in places, and the surface quakes under ones feet. The moss formed over an area of Ice Age deposition, where stream-borne gravels form a terrace over a mile long and about six feet high. Sinuous ridges of gravel known as eskers link up with the terrace, and its surface is pitted with small rounded depressions or kettle-holes. Because of this surface irregularity, wet *Sphagnum* bogs and pools now alternate with drier grassy ridges which are heavily grazed by rabbits and sheep. Inbetween are groups of pine and thickets of birch and willow. At least thirty species of birds regularly nest on the moss, including fifty pairs of Common Gull. Leuchar Moss qualifies in many ways as the wildest piece of ground in Aberdeen District. It may not survive as such for very much longer, unfortunately. The main drains have recently been cleaned, and a EEC grant-aided land improvement scheme appears to be underway.

Two miles east of Leuchar Moss is a much smaller but scarcely less wild patch of wetland in a hollow between three farms. I have never visited this site, but a friend has described it as 'a wilderness reminiscent of the everglades', full of dense thickets of birch and moribund willows. Stumbling through this jungle, my friend completely lost his way, and when he eventually emerged, bedraggled and wet, he found that he had strayed back in a circle to his starting point. It is good to know that a few such places still exist in Aberdeen District.

Near the northern boundary of the District is a second large area of wet heath, a peat-filled basin known as *Grandhome Moss*. Parts of Grandhome are almost as wet as Leuchar Moss: the lowest parts of the valley consist of deep cushions of *Sphagnum* in which one sinks up to the knee. Some of the moss is an odd mixture of birch woodland and bog, the trees being perched on grassy tussocks standing amid the peat bogs and pools. The edges of the moss consist of large areas of heather, crowberry, rushes and poor grassland, with scattered birch and rowan. Parts of the edge of the moss have been afforested or are used as rough grazing. Aberdeen City has advanced rapidly towards Grandhome Moss in recent years, and its neighbourhood is now one of suburban development. The almost inevitable consequence of this is that the nearby heathland 'wastes' are used by local residents as a convenient rubbish dump, and by developers and public authorities as a tipping ground. A small but botanically very rich area of wet heath and birch-willow woodland known as *Arnhall Moss* near Westhills is perhaps the most threatened of all, since it has been all but engulfed by the vast new housing estate nearby. Fortunately, in this case some local residents have 'adopted' the moss as a backdoor nature reserve, and look after it. This is perhaps the best hope for such fragile sites: Once the land is felt to *belong* to the local community, there is some hope for its survival; as 'waste ground' there is no hope at all.

Most breeding birds of heathland and marsh recorded from the neighbourhood of Aberdeen in the past hundred years are still with us, albeit in much reduced numbers. One which has disappeared is the Twite. This little finch, whose peculiar world distribution consists of the Tibetan steppes and the Atlantic coast of north west Europe, was once said to be 'fairly abundant on moor and marsh' near Aberdeen. Its apparent 'disappearance' may be a simple case of mistaken identity, however. The Twite is difficult to identify, except by voice and the early ornithologists would not have had the benefit of binoculars. It may be significant that Aberdeen's greatest naturalist, William MacGillivray thought that Hebridean Linnets were Twites, until he moved to the east, and saw the real thing for the first time.

Two of the most startling discoveries in Aberdeen's natural history were made on its heaths, and both, unfortunately, turned out to be bogus. The first of these was a very modest-looking sedge called *Carex davalliana*, whose one melancholy distinction is that it was among the first known plants in the British flora to become extinct. It grew only on a bog near Bath, and disappeared forever during drainage operations there in the 1830s. James Beattie, the then Professor of Civil and Natural History at Aberdeen, must therefore have been both surprised and excited when he found what he believed was this sedge during a visit to Stocket Moor in 1800. His find was officially confirmed by Smith, the expert who had first discovered and described the sedge. Quite independently, *C davalliana* was also recorded on the Links below Broadhill by an amateur botanist called Mr Cow. Mr Cow was subsequently shown to be wildly inaccurate in his naming of plants, but if both finds were widely known, many might have regarded this very rare plant as a native of Aberdeen. Fortunately Beattie left a detailed description of the locality of his sedge and his specimens had been preserved in the herbarium of the Linnaean Society. When they were carefully examined at a later date, it soon became apparent that Beattie and Smith were mistaken. The Stocket Moor sedge was not *davalliana* but a relatively common relative, the Dioecious Sedge. A trip to the moor in Beattie's footsteps soon confirmed that the latter species was growing in abundance by the banks of a little rill at the very place where Beattie had 'discovered' *davalliana*. The reason for Beattie's mistake was probably that *C davalliana* was so rare and unfamiliar, that most botanists had no clear idea of what it looked like; then, as now, wishful thinking can work wonders.

A similar instance in the entomological world, placed Scotstown Moor on the moth hunter's map for nearly seventy years. James Duncan, a local collector who was eventually to leave a superb collection to the university, took an unusual moth at Scotstown Moor in 1908, which he identified as the Marsh Moth, an insect of (as was then thought) almost fabulous rarity and hitherto known only from the fens of East Anglia. This dull orange moth won renown as 'the jewel in the crown of Scotstown Moor', and it established the area as A Locality. That no-one else ever found the moth was ascribed to its elusive habits. Only recently was the Marsh Moth Myth laid to rest, when Duncan's specimen was traced and critically examined by local entomologists Robert Palmer and Mark Young. The specimen had somehow or other lost its abdomen, so that the diagnostic features of the genitalia could not be checked, but its wing patterns certainly did not tally with those of the true Marsh Moth, a species which possibly Duncan had never seen. The trouble was that they did not tally precisely with any other moth either. The concensus of opinion, however, was that Duncan's moth was an unusual colour variety of a relatively common species.

Chapter 7

Open Water and the Coast

Aberdeen's coastline forms two strongly contrasting sections, which are neatly divided by the mouth of the Dee. The soft sandy shore between the Don and the Dee was almost wholly reclaimed over sixty years ago (see Chapter Two), and given over to the sports and amusements of the human inhabitants of the nearby city and its summer visitors. The rocky coast to the south of the Dee has proved more resistant to change and, once one has passed the coastguard station at Greg Ness, the cliff scenery is almost as wild and unspoilt as if it were thirty, rather than three miles from the city centre. In consequence, this stretch of coast is one of the most interesting haunts for wildlife in the District, and a surprisingly large proportion of the wild plants and animals of the north eastern coast can be found within easy reach of Aberdeen.

THE SANDY SHORE

In Chapter Two, we followed the transformation of the city's shoreline from a region of natural sandhills into an almost wholly urbanised recreation ground. Most of the native plant life had already been eliminated by about 1920, but improvements to coastal defences and public amenities continued to be made. By 1963, a sea wall and lines of groynes stretched along the entire beach front from Dee to Don. The original dune ridge was levelled and buried throughout its length, except for a small sand spit at Donmouth. In its place, a barrier of pre-cast concrete with a public promenade slopes up to a bank of sown grass leading in turn to the esplanade. Nearer the Don, the concrete wall is replaced by rubble-filled gabions and panels of steel mesh, through which a few rank plants such as Lyme Grass and Curled Dock manage to poke their heads. New embryo dunes covered in Lyme Grass have formed in places beneath the wall, but these are ephemeral features which could be removed by a single storm. Between them, the sea-wall and the groynes have prevented almost all natural movement and accumulation of sand and sediment, and consequently today's beach is quite different from that of a century ago. At that time it was said to be narrow, with a tidal 'ridge and runnel' system, similar to that on the beach between the Don and the Ythan. Now it is wide and flat, and at high tide the sea reaches right up to the sea wall. It has been calculated that about 2,800,000 cubic metres of sand have been removed by the tides from the original beach, during the past century![1]

Driving along the beach carriageway, one passes broken fragments of sand dunes sandwiched uneasily between the golf courses and the road. These have a thick covering of Marram Grass and patches of whin scrub, but they are too small and degraded to provide refuges for many of the original duneland plants. Flowers such as Yellow Goats-beard, Sand Meadow-rue and Sea Pansy still persist in such places, but the community and pattern of the original vegetation, together with most of its interest to botanists, has long since gone. The only exception is the Donmouth sand spit. This little snakes-head of shingle and sand has been called 'the most dynamic spit-bar-beach complex between Stonehaven and Fraserburgh'.[2] Aerial photographs taken over a period of several years show that the spit is twisting and turning in a serpentine way, whose main emphasis is to move gradually northwards. This process of sand building was reversed in 1978, when the head of the spit was cut off by changes in the current, but in 1980 the building process resumed again: sand is eroded from the dunes north of the Don, creating abrupt sand cliffs above high water mark, and deposited by long shore drift onto the south bank. Centuries of similar sand-shifting has brought the Don estuary to a position at least a mile north of its original position.

The lower part of the spit has been disfigured by the dumping of rubble and other material, but the upper part, at least, is a natural sandbank despite its cobweb of paths and heavy use at times by holidaymakers. The sand has been colonised by dense Lyme Grass tussocks. Lyme Grass has a competitive edge over Marram Grass on broken and embryo dunes, probably because it can better tolerate an occasional flooding of salt water.

The tidal basin sheltering on the lee-side of the sand spit was the last refuge of many salt marsh plants which were once widespread in the Don estuary. Unfortunately the area of tidal inundation has been much reduced lately through the landscaping of the estuarine banks, and what were once patches of comparatively natural vegetation have since become swards of smooth lawn grass. Whether wild flowers of salt

1 Ritchie, Smith and Rose (1978).
2 ibid.

pasture such as Sea Milkwort or Sea Spurrey can tolerate the present conditions remains to be seen, but their long-term prospects of survival in the Don estuary must be slim.

North of the estuary stretches a continuous beach and dune ridge, forming a smooth ten mile crescent of sand between the Don and the Ythan, of which only the southernmost quarter lies within Aberdeen District. The whole of the latter area is given over to golfing and fishing interests, but its overall use is much less intensive than that of the Aberdeen Links and it is less modified from its original condition. From the Bridge of Don northwards, there is a 'wild' dune ridge rising to forty feet above sea level, behind which are a series of hollows. The original heath sward behind the dune ridge has long since been reclaimed for the Royal Aberdeen and Murcar golf courses, and the drainage of wet hollows a century ago resulted in the loss of some local specialities, such as Baltic Rush and Curved Sedge (see page 35).

The dunes nearest to Aberdeen at the Bridge of Don are badly eroded in places, both by natural processes and by the passage of many hundreds of pairs of human feet. At least one bird no longer nests here in consequence. This is the Litttle Tern, which is undergoing a nationwide decrease in numbers, since the subtle mixtures of pebbles and sand which are its favoured nesting site, are also often favoured localities for human beings on holiday. Only in the comparative seclusion of the Sands of Forvie and St Cyrus National Nature Reserves does the Little Tern continue to breed in moderate numbers, and even here it is plagued by a variety of natural enemies, such as kestrels, foxes and storm tides.

Despite the loss of its rarest and most sensitive species, the dunes between the Don and Blackdog Burn continue to support much of their indigenous flora and associated flora. One indication of a fairly healthy duneland environment is the recorded occurence here of a trio of coastal moths: the Sand Dart, the Coast Dart and the White Colon. Each occupies a slightly different part of the dunes. The Sand Dart, which was discovered hereabouts in 1975, lives down on the foreshore, just above the high tide mark, where its caterpillars require a plentiful growth of Sea Rocket and other strand-line plants. The Coast Dart, on the other hand, occurs some distance behind the foreshore on the open Marram Grass dunes, especially where flowers are plentiful. And it is flowers, particularly those of the Rest-harrow, which form food for the caterpillars of the White Colon moth. The Sand Dart which, to the connoisseur at least, is a delectable and desirable moth, is dependant on the presence of embryo foreshore dunes, and therefore must shift its ground from year to year in accordance with the natural movements of the sand.

Curiously enough, in view of its very precise environmental niche, its caterpillar can be reared in a bucket of sand, on nothing more elaborate than a steady diet of sliced carrot.

Since public access to the Links is almost confined to the beach, the dunes become increasingly less disturbed as one walks northwards away from Aberdeen. But the walker who does not know the area is in for a rude surprise when he reaches the District boundary at Blackdog, for here the City is back with a vengeance. Blackdog is a Corporation tipping area. The natural dune profile in the vicinity of Blackdog Burn has been virtually obliterated by the tipping of industrial refuse and slurry waste, while immediately to the north is an old sand quarry which has been backfilled by rubble and spoil. 'Official' tipping ceased in 1979 and since this is one of the few places near Aberdeen where the beach is accessible to the motor car, its future, once the surface is restored, is probably that of a high density recreation area along the lines of Aberdeen Links. The main obstacle to these designs is a deep slurry pool lurking below a refuse tip which is said to be almost impossible to drain without 'special treatment'. The banks of the Blackdog Burn, which still contain a varied assemblage of marshland plants, including the rare Water Whorl-grass, are likely to fall victim to any future improvement of the surrounding ground.

The coastal dunes from Bridge of Don to Newburgh are the subject of a proposed Country Park, and a detailed landscape survey was undertaken by Grampian Regional Council in 1977. So far as the area within Aberdeen City District is concerned, such designation is unlikely to make any difference to the way in which the dunes are managed. The entire area is one of private golf courses, bounded at one end by a polluted estuary and at the other by a refuse tip and a MOD firing range. Country Park or no Country Park, these links are already fully booked.

THE ROCKY SHORE

Aberdeen's wild coastal cliff scenery from Greg Ness down to Cove Bay is a world apart from the endless golf courses and urban entertainments of its soft shores. It is, on the other hand, an area full of contradictions, an uneasy blend of past and present. At Cove Bay, small boats bring in lobsters and crabs, and a fisherman hangs up his nets to dry, as he has done for centuries. And yet this fisherman's next door neighbour is a commuter who services the oil industry whose warehouses lie not much more than a stone's throw away. Both live in nineteenth century stone bothies stuffed full of mod cons, a combination as incongruous as a jet-propelled stage coach, whilst the new houses sprouting up like mushrooms seem designed to look as much like old bothies as modern building materials and design idioms will allow. Aberdeen's rocky shore is not a place where people go to 'get away from it all' but, to adapt a phrase coined by Nan Fairbrother, where they can get '*half* away from *some* of it'.

Likewise, the rocky coast does not retain its wildness and rugged appeal by accident, but by the strenuous efforts of teams of townsmen working from the top of a skyscraper. District plans include the coastline from Girdleness to Souter Head within Loirston Country Park, while the greater part of the remainder is designated either as a Conservation Area or as a Site of Special Scientific Interest. The most useful manifestation of this plethora of labelling is the improved footpath which runs along the full length of the cliff top as far as Cove Bay, and places the entire area within reach of anyone willing to use his legs. This is fortunate indeed, because there is a great deal to see.

The dramatic outline of the cliffs is the product of their complex geology. They are composed of a mixture of ancient metamorphic and igneous rocks, such as schists and gneisses, capped by a layer of glacial clay or till. The characteristic features of these cliffs are the narrow chasms known as 'yawns' or 'geos'. They are formed by the erosion of narrow dykes of softer volcanic material within the hard rocks of the cliffs. At Doonie's Yawn the chasm has been 'plugged' at the landward end by a mass of glacial boulder clay. At Cove Bay there is a large wave-cut rock platform which exposes an unusually wide range of metamorphic rocks, including andalusite, sillimanite and garnet. Part of this platform has been artificially strengthened into a harbour pier, which protects the little shingle beach beneath the village.

The flora of the cliffs is varied and interesting. The cliff top itself is springy grassland of Red Fescue with Crowberry and wind-pruned heather taking over on the more exposed tops. Its soils are derived from the capping of glacial till, rather than the bedrock, and since the former derives from the calcium-rich sandstones of Strathmore, the cliffs often form refuges for lime-loving plants, as well as those characteristic of salt-sprayed cliffs. The lime lovers include colourful beauties such as Purple Milk-vetch, Meadow Saxifrage, Burnet Rose, Bloody Cranesbill and Rock-rose, which tend to favour the more open places on the cliffs, where there is a thinner covering of soil. This often provides them with the additional benefit of inaccessibility. Among the salt spray specialists, Thrift and the two maritime plantains, Sea and Bucks-horn, are plentiful, whilst in some of the shadier rocky bays, a coastal fern, the Sea Spleenwort grows from crevices in the rock. The Sea Spleenwort has shiny, deep green fronds, a characteristic shared by the leaves of Scurvy Grass and Lovage. which occur above the splash zone on the rocky headlands. The leaves of Scurvy Grass and Lovage are sharp tasting and rich in vitamin C, and were once gathered for salads. My own experiments in this field suggest that while Lovage makes a not unpleasant nibble on a hot day, Scurvy Grass leaves are variable in taste, but invariably revolting. Perhaps they tasted differently in the past. The Lovage has a curious distribution in Britain. Although it is fairly common on Scotland's rocky coasts, it virtually ceases to grow once the English border is crossed. It would make a better candidate than the ubiquitous thistle for Scotland's national emblem.

Two particularly interesting plants used to occur on the cliffs near Cove Bay. One of these was the Royal Fern, that sumptuous and archaic plant of the Atlantic coast, which grew 'on steep rocks' and 'by the side of a waterfall'. This locality seems to have been the last stand of the Royal Fern in the north east, for it was reported as extinct as early as the mid-nineteenth century in its boggy, inland localities. For many years a few plants hung on at Cove but, so far as I am aware, no living person has seen it there. Its decline was almost certainly due to the once fashionable sport of fern collecting. The other Cove speciality was the Mossy Saxifrage which, according to Dickie, was 'discovered by a lady' in 1859. The Mossy Saxifrage is almost exclusively a plant of high mountains, but it does occur wild in at least one place on the Banff coast, which invites the interesting speculation that the Cove plants may also have been indigenous. It is an attractive enough flower to be widely grown in garden rockeries however, and since the saxifrage, like the Royal Fern, has not been seen at Cove Bay for many years, it is possible that we shall never know whether they were truly wild or merely garden escapes.

Cove is one of three places along the Kincardineshire coast which are noted 'localities' for insects, and it is by far the best known site near Aberdeen. It has attracted beetle specialists and flea hunters in the past, but the area is best known for its butterflies and moths. These include species which are widespread in southern England, but which are more or less confined to the coast in Scotland: examples include the Grayling butterfly, the Cinnabar moth and the Common Footman (which ought perhaps, to be renamed the Rare Footman, north of the Border). Many of Cove's special moths have lyrical names: there is poetry in the Feathered Gothic or the Thrift Clearwing, whilst a trio of fairly dim moths known respectively as The Confused, The Suspected and The Anomalous, suggest that even experienced entomologists sometimes have difficulty telling one from another.

A diversity of wild flowers tends to mean a diversity of insects, and that is no doubt the reason why Cove is particularly rich. Behind this confident assertion, however, lie many problems. There is an abundance of Rock-rose at Cove, and this explains the presence of a very local moth, the Square-spot Dart, but it does not explain the absence of the Northern Brown Argus butterfly, which likewise depends on Rock-rose. Then there is the case of a tiny moth with a very long name, *Agonopterix alstromeriana*. The caterpillar of *Agonopterix* is thought to feed entirely on Hemlock, which, so far as we know, does not occur at Cove, and yet the moth is common enough and is unlikely to be an immigrant. Nature is full of such minor mysteries.

There is less mystery surrounding the disappearance of Cove's best known insect, the Small Blue butterfly. This pretty little insect, Britain's smallest butterfly, requires an abundance of Kidney Vetch among which to lay its eggs, and this tends to confine it to open, lime-rich places such as downland, railway verges and cliffs. Its locality at Cove used to be in the disused quarry between The Kettle and Colsea Yawn, where its foodplant grew in abundance. Unfortunately holes in the ground near Aberdeen are regarded by public authorities and private developers alike as open-air dustbins. Between 1974 and 1975, the quarry was infilled by an agreement between its owner and the Aberdeen and Kincardine Cleansing Departments and that was the end of the Small Blue. By the time conservationists were alerted to the scene, the damage was done. The crowning irony to this foul deed is that the new Academy of Cove Bay is adopting the Small Blue butterfly as a motif for its school badge.

The cliffs within Aberdeen City District do not contain large seabird colonies like those south of Stonehaven but, apart from the ever-present gulls, feral pigeons and Jackdaws, there are small numbers of nesting Kittiwakes, Razorbills and Fulmars. The Fulmar is a comparatively recent arrival. Writing in 1901, George Sim regarded it as 'a straggler that is by no means of common occurence'. The spectacular spread of the Fulmar to colonise most of the rocky shores of Britain is thought to be due to an invasion of Icelandic birds, which followed in the wake of trawlers and whaling vessels. The Fulmar is currently prospecting the suitability of houses in Stonehaven as potential nesting sites, and it is possible that it may eventually join the Herring Gull and Oyster-catcher on Aberdeen's roof-tops.

A few pairs of House Martins at Cove Bay prefer to nest on cliff headlands rather than nearby houses. Cliffs both inland and coastal must have been the original habitat of the House Martin but, since it is an opportunist bird, not averse to sharing a house with human beings, the number of places where it has retained its ancestral habits are relatively few. In the ancient days when all House Martins nested on cliffs, there may have been breeding White-tailed Eagles in this area. The local name for this huge bird was an 'Erne', and a memory of a long-lost nest site is preserved in the name of Earnsheugh Bay at Findon. Our local Ernes had probably deserted the area by 1600, and certainly they had gone long before local people began to take an interest in non-edible birds. The last recorded specimen was a vagrant which collided into Girdleness Lighthouse in 1853.

The Tystie or Black Guillemot may once have been a fairly common breeding bird on the rocky costline near Aberdeen. Sim states that it may have bred at Cove Bay and the cliffs to the south as late as 1834, but that it disappeared soon afterwards. It continued to be seen commonly outside Aberdeen harbour in the nineteenth century, but the Tystie is now no more than an occasional visitor to Aberdeen's shores.

Grey seals are quite common on Aberdeen's rocky shores and sandy beach in the summer. On the latter they can sometimes be seen sitting in shallow water, eating large salmon like bananas. The Common Porpoise is also sometimes seen close inshore, although they have become rarer here in the past thirty years, as have the larger North Sea whales. When whales were more common, a century ago, there are reports of an occasional luckless animal becoming stranded on the beach or entangled in salmon nets. In 1870, for instance, a Great Fin Whale and a Lesser Fin Whale were caught in the nets, to the great delight of Dr Struthers, a local Professor of Anatomy, whose hobby it was to dissect their vast malodorous carcasses.

Thus far we have a coastal flora and fauna which is interesting enough, but in no way unique. There is however one wild plant on this part of Aberdeen's coast which at the time of writing, is known with certainty from nowhere else in Britain. This is the delicate rock fern, *Cystopteris dickieana*, known by the vulgar as Dickie's Bladder-fern. *Dickieana* is a mysterious plant in several ways. The first published reference to it is in Dr Dickie's Flora Abredonensis of 1838, and the fern was subsequently named in his honour. Not long after its discovery, the fern abruptly disappeared: in 1860, Dickie wrote that 'having been the first to distribute specimens in a living state, among cultivators, my name has been associated with this singular variety ... It is now completely extirpated'. The Victorians had a rabid craze for fern collecting, and once word got around, everyone must have wanted a specimen of the new variety. Fortunately Dickie was wrong, but numbers of his eponymous fern must have been very low for, sixty years later, Trail's Flora records that it was 'nearly extinct'. From that low point, it has recovered quite well. A year ago I counted sixty six clumps, totalling a thousand or more separate fronds growing among shady crevices in the rock. Perhaps it is not entirely without significance that most of these plants were out of reach... The fern is now officially classed as 'endangered' in Britain, and has recently been afforded legal protection under the Wildlife and Countryside Act (1981). This provides for penalties up to £100 for picking or uprooting a specimen. Because of the rarity of *dickieana*, I have been deliberately vague about the locality. It is conceivable, however, that *dickieana* may not be so rare after all. It is a 'problem' plant which was long classed as a mere variety, and the qualities which separate it as a full species are based largely on technical, microscopic features. Although most botanists who have seen it in the wild (and I suspect they are rather few in number - Aberdeen is off the botanical beaten track) would agree that it nevertheless *looks* distinct enough, it might very easily escape attention if it was growing in a place where one was not expecting to find it. As it is, plants which are genetically similar to the Aberdeen *dickieana* have been found in two places in Perthshire and one in Cornwall. This is a peculiar distribution to say the least, and the most obvious explanation is that is has been under-recorded. Most Aberdonian naturalists will, I am sure, hope that this is not the case.

If a stranger to the shores of Aberdeen read the foregoing account, he or she might well receive the impression that man has scarcely altered the natural character of the sea cliffs. He has, of course, and the intensity of that alteration increases as one nears Aberdeen. Man's main impact has been to quarry and to tip refuse - usually in that order, since the worked-out quarries become in turn prime sites for the wastes of the city. Apart from the official private and Corporation tips, far too many slopes and gullies sport their own sad trail of tin cans, rusting cars and agricultural waste, wherever a sufficiently selfish person has been able to back his lorry up to the cliff face. Even the picture postcard harbour at Cove Bay possesses its own eyesore.

The big tips lie immediately south of Nigg Bay. The bay itself is currently the scene of frenetic activity: a construction plant is busy improving the Long Sea Outfall, that lengthy pipe which cheerfully squirts raw sewage out to sea as though our oceans were a bottomless pit; in the background, diesel lorries roar up to Tullos Hill bearing heavy loads of pulverised refuse. Amid these rather grim surroundings is one of the most important geological sites in Grampian region. The low cliffs in the southern angle of Nigg Bay contain evidence which has helped scientists to unravel the history of Ice Age glaciations in the north east, although the interpretation of this evidence is still a matter of controversy. The cliff section has two layers of glacial clay or till, one red and the other grey, both of which contain boulders and gravels thought to be of Scandinavian origin, and which provide evidence of a link between north east Scotland and northern Europe during the Ice Age. Unfortunately the lower part of this section is no longer accessible and the remainder has been obscured. This part of the bay had been eroded by the tides, which presented a serious threat to the coast road above the cliff-top. 'Selected material' was therefore used as a defensive measure to ballast the shoreline, thus effectively burying much of the geological evidence. Paradoxically, this may help to preserve the section from continued erosion, so that at least the geologist of the distant future may be able to examine it with, presumably, superior techniques and knowledge. The tipping could therefore be described as a conservation measure!

The coastal defence works at Nigg attracted a great deal of unauthorised tipping by contractors and this led many to assume that this area was a Council rubbish tip. The modern City tips all lie to the west of the railway line, however, although some of that uncovered rubbish is sometimes blown coastwards. The cliff tops south of Greg Ness were used as a private tip. This is no longer active and has since been levelled, but a slurry pit, crusted with scum like ancient porridge, still lurks evilly near one of the most attractive parts of the cliffs. Where they have been left unsown by agricultural grass mixtures, these old tips are gradually being vegetated naturally by a mixture of colonist weeds and indigenous coastal plants. In the latter category, Scurvy Grass, which seems to be able to tolerate almost any conditions providing there is sufficient salt in the soil, is the outright winner, but Scentless Mayweed and Thrift run it close. Quite a long list could be made of the colonisers. They include an abundance of Coltsfoot, a useful plant whose long roots pull up trace elements from the depths to nourish the impoverished soil at the surface. Others which thrive in and give colour to these arid surroundings include Silverweed, Field Horsetail, Wild Pansy, Cow Parsley and, of course, those monarchs of the tip, the Willow-herbs.

OPEN WATERS

There is probably less open water in Aberdeen City today than at any other time in its history. When Aberdeen's two natural lochs were drained during the Age of Improvement, they were to some extent replaced by numerous industrial mill dams and the Aberdeen-Inverurie canal. Deeper pools also formed at the base of most disused quarries, whilst, on a smaller scale, there was no shortage of wells, water butts and puddles, from which Dickie's Flora contains an imposing catalogue of aquatic algae and diatoms. The mill dams made excellent artificial ponds, and places such as Rubislaw bleach works and Gilcomston dam were 'localities' on the beaten track of botanical excursions. When water ceased to form the basis of industrial power, however, these ponds were filled in, and few were left by 1920. Many of the quarry ponds survive, but these dark rocky pools were always of less interest, and they soon became the focus of refuse tipping.

There is no longer any industrial requirement for ponds, and almost the only places in the city where a pond can hope to remain unpolluted for long is in parks or school grounds. Here, it could be argued, they would provide a haven of solace for harassed workers and an interesting haunt for school classes, as well as a place where frogs, newts and dragonflies could continue to breed. Unfortunately, with one or two exceptions, it is not the city's policy to construct ponds, since they are regarded as risks to human life. The fate of the ponds of Stewart Park typify this attitude. In the words of the park booklet,

'Part of the land contained two quarries, later turned into trout ponds and, after a while, duck ponds. However, because of possible danger to young children these ponds were filled in and planted over'.

While such action is understandable in the case of dangerous quarries, shallow pools well fringed with willows and sedges scarcely warrant the appellation of death traps. It would be just as logical to argue against planting trees, in case a child climbs them and falls off, or against planting poisonous daffodils, in case a child eats one. There seems to be an element of doublethink in the way ponds are regarded, for in one of the few cases where an urban park does have a pond, the booklet earnestly invites us to admire the aquatic plants and to 'look for the small aquatic beetles and insects that live in the pond.' To be consistent, they should either invite us to detest the beetles or provide more of them.

One park at the edge of the city has a pond as its centrepiece however: *Walker Dam*. Its miraculous preservation is due to a family of swans which inhabit its waters and were left a legacy providing for their protection during the breeding season. Walker Dam was regarded as one of the best localities near Aberdeen at the turn of the century. It is part of entomological lore, since it is known as a locality for a rare water beetle, *Agabus biguttatus*. In this case, its fame is probably undeserved, for the beetle's presence here rests on a single unconfirmed record, which local experts now regard as probably wrong anyway. Walker Dam is otherwise an attractive but unremarkable silty pond which provides some minnows, tadpoles and whirligigs for local schoolchildren to fish for. Nearby, there are surviving fragments of original woodland with alder, hazel and sallows. A small patch of marshy ground on the southern shore has been left alone and contains Bottle Sedge and Reed Canary Grass, and is one of a handful of places in the north east where the attractive grass, *Glyceria plicata*, has been found.

Ponds and lochs become slightly more frequent as one leaves the confines of the city. At Hazlehead, there is a duck pond, as well as the concrete tank by the restaurant, whilst on Scotstown Moor at Denmore, there is a tiny pool which teems with life. This pond is little more than a hole in the ground, like a shell crater, with bare earthern banks, yet it contains an excellent variety of water beetles and bugs, with a number of unusual species. The most bizarre of these is probably the Water Scorpion, whose 'sting' is really a breathing tube, and whose drab dun-coloured wings hide a startling red and black body. Other special-ities include the large and ferocious Diving Beetle, *Dytiscus*, and the equally large, frightening and completely harmless Horse Leech. The reason for the variety of life in this particular pool may be its lush growth of Canadian Pondweed, *Elodea*. This pondweed was introduced into Britain in the mid-nineteenth century, and spread rapidly through the then nationwide network of canals. Unlike many successful 'aliens', it provides a good habitat for native animals. In the pool on Scotstown Moor it freely produces its unusual flowers: little floating cups attached to the plant by a long thread-like stalk. For some reason, nearly all the *Elodea* flowers in Britain are female. The lesson of this little pool is surely that a pond does not need to be at all elaborate, to attract an interesting range of animals. Two Council workmen equipped with shovels could create a similar one in a day; then all they would need to do is wait for things to happen.

At the opposite end of the open water scale is *Loirston Loch*. An island of blue in the midst of the unlovely parish of Nigg, this is the largest body of freshwater in the vicinity of Aberdeen. Its bare shores are fully exposed on all sides, and the only cover is provided by a few willow bushes and two small reedbeds; indeed, from a distance it looks like a gigantic puddle. The stark scene is not improved by the A956 which slices along the east side of the loch on an embankment, cutting off and isolating a small pool on the opposite side. It is this uncompromis-ing setting which is referred to in the Loirston Country Park booklet as 'the attractive waters of Loirston Loch'. Is it perhaps an indication of how ugly our modern world has become, or is it just a falling off of critical standards, that anyone could describe this bleak, naked loch as 'attractive'? Eighty years ago, George Sim was less polite about it: 'ugly in the extreme ... surrounded by mounds of boulder drift, while the bottom is strewn with innumerable blocks of coarse granite and gneiss.' This desolation was relieved only by a few 'stunted, starving firs'. Sim would find even less to commend it now. The oil age has over-taken Loirston Loch and it now lies in the heart of an area in chaotic transition from agriculture to industry. Dead and dying farms litter the surrounding land, whilst sleek new warehouses peep up from over the hill.

Despite its aesthetic shortcomings, Loirston Loch has retained a remarkably full complement of wetland plants and birds. On the shore below the road embankment, where it is protected from grazing, there are a variety of marsh flowers such as Northern Marsh Orchid, Marsh Cinquefoil, Water Forget-me-not and Brooklime. The small reed bed around the inflow streams is made up not of the true reed, but of the superficially similar Reed Sweet Grass, together with Bottle Sedge. The remaining banks are trampled and churned up by cattle, but even here there are a variety of small sedges and small, unobtrusive plants such as Marsh Pennywort among the chewed grass. The hard, stony waters of the loch are shallow and well vegetated with a large moss, *Fontinalis*, Common Spike-rush and various kinds of linear and broad-leaved Pondweeds. Other true aquatics include Shore-weed, a thick-leaved rosette plant related to the plantains, which flowers only when uncovered by the water in the driest months. Together with the pleasant pink blossoms of Amphibious Persicaria, Shore-weed covers large parts of the loch in the summer; harder to find are the Small Bur-reed and the Bogbean, which are present only in small quantity. Several of the forementioned plants are now rather rare near Aberdeen, but this is because of the scarcity of unpolluted pools and wet ground, rather than any inherent scarcity of the plants themselves.

One plant which occurs near Loirston Loch can claim to be a national rarity however. This is an unobtrusive little rush which looks not unlike a piece of green wire, and has given the appropriate name of Thread Rush. It was originally found here one hundred and thirty years ago by George Dickie, and Loirston Loch remains its only known locality in the north east. Several recent search parties failed to find the Thread Rush in the place where it formerly grew, and for a time it was feared extinct. In 1980, however, Christopher Ferreira and J Grant Roger stumbled upon scores of Thread Rushes bristling in the turf in an other-wise very ordinary patch of wet ground. It seems probable, in fact, that the Thread Rush shifts its ground from time to time, for it requires areas of bare mud to establish, and cannot tolerate much competition from other plants. Its main habitat elsewhere in Britain is the muddy banks of newly constructed reservoirs, where it can suddenly appear from nowhere, and equally suddenly disappear again. It is more than probable that its seeds are eaten and transported by birds. If so, we have in the Thread Rush another 'opportunist', albeit not a very successful one, capable of exploiting man-made habitats. Paradoxically it is probably the trampling of cattle around the margins of Loirston Loch which provide a sufficient amount of wet mud for the species to have maintained itself there for so long.

Loirston's waters are fished by the Aberdeen Angling Association, who have stocked it with Common and Rainbow Trout. It is also full of Perch, which grow to a good size and must have been introduced at some point in the distant past. The only truely indigenous fish in the loch are the Eel and the Stickleback. The loch attracts birdwatchers and a good variety of breeding and wintering wildfowl can often be seen there - without the need to stray from the comfort of one's car. Up to a hundred Mallard and seventy Tufted Duck use the loch in winter, and fifteen Whooper Swans were counted in November 1974. Smaller numbers of Wigeon, Pochard, Goldeneye, Teal, Scaup, Pintail and Great Crested Grebe are also more or less regularly seen. It is not a great place for rarities, although a Buffle-headed Duck, was 'said to be shot (there) in January 1865'. The nesting birds of the loch are unremarkable: Mallard, Tufted Duck, Coot and Moorhen, whilst the reedbeds are utilised by Reed Bunting and Sedge Warbler.

Many of Loirston's wild duck must suffer agonies from a small, brownish leech called *Theromyzon*, which occurs in the loch. *Theromyzon* has an unpleasant habit of crawling into the nostrils of water birds where it gorges on the blood of their nasal cavities - sometimes with fatal consequences for the bird. Little is otherwise known of the invertebrate life of Loirston Loch; some might say the less known, the better: invertebrates lives are sometimes almost too much to bear!

Beyond the suburbs and the industrial estates of Aberdeen, there is greater variety of open water. There are lakes of private houses such as Parkhill, dammed up streams such as Culter Compensation Dam and Hillhead, and natural lochs at Skene and Newtonhill. Farm ponds, on the other hand, seem to have almost disappeared from the District, since water for livestock is now almost universally piped. Most of the forementioned lochs are too thoroughly rural to form detailed subjects for this book, except perhaps for poor Stoneywood House loch, nestling beneath the frowning walls of the Stoneywood paper mill. This loch does not seem to be visited very often by naturalists, but it does form one of only three stations in the County for the Long-stalked Pondweed, which indicates that it is of reasonable quality.

The most important open water bodies near Aberdeen are undoubtedly Corby, Lily and Bishops Lochs, which lie side by side in a natural basin east of Parkhill. This trio, sometimes known collectively as the Triple Lochs, are curiously inaccessible, hidden away in what, until recently, was deepest countryside. Aberdeen has spread so rapidly in their direction in the past few years, that the Triple Lochs have become almost suburban and have been candidates for a Country Park and a Local Nature Reserve. Their history is described separately in Chapter Nine.

Chapter 8

Emissaries from Afar

Aberdeen has the reputation of being a Mecca for migratory birds. This is in part, the consequence of its having a large, resident and active population of birdwatchers but, even so, there can be very few other towns in Britain which have two sites of the highest quality within easy walking distance of the city centre, as there are at Girdleness and Donmouth. Before examining these sites in detail, however, let us look at some of the more characteristic migrants to visit Aberdeen.

The off-shore passage of birds often provides good things for those with powerful binoculars. There is a large annual passage of auks and divers, with peak numbers in January, and ocean birds like shearwaters and skuas can turn up in small numbers at other times. The most important gathering of sea birds near Aberdeen is the flock of sea ducks which gather annually to moult between Donmouth and Blackdog Links, at a distance of between a quarter of a mile and a mile off-shore. The flock, which gathers between June and October, contains up to ten thousand Eiders and one thousand Common and Velvet Scoters, and this is regarded as a nationally important concentration. In their flightless condition, these sea ducks are particularly vulnerable to oil spillage at that time of year.

As befits its northerly position, Aberdeen is particularly well-known for its winter visitors from Iceland, Scandinavia and the Arctic. The most thoroughly urban of these is the Waxwing, which can be found throughout the city in a good year, wherever there are late autumn berries like Cotoneaster and Whitebeam. I have always associated Waxwings with university campuses, and the area between Old Aberdeen and Powis Academy certainly seems to get more than its fair share of them. A flock of Waxwings shrilling among the bushes as they gorge themselves with berries, apparently oblivious of the human onlooker, is one of the great compensations of winter. Of course not every year is a Waxwing year. The good Waxwing winter of 1975/76 was followed by two years in which scarcely any were seen at all. More regular in its appearances, but less often seen by the average townsman, is the Snow

Bunting, which flocks on what is left of the dunes on the Donmouth sand spit. On Cairngorm, this beautiful little finch has adopted vulgar habits, pecking among the skiers crisp packets and cast-off sandwiches as though it were a common sparrow, but Aberdeen's birds are resolutely non-urban. The Snow Bunting's chosen haunts in Aberdeen are not without their hazards, unfortunately. It was in this area of the Links that Sim records a Great Grey Shrike, 'caught by a man who was snaring larks and linnets'. The catching of wild song birds is now illegal but not unknown, and Snow Buntings are said to be among the main victims at Aberdeen.

The big, pale Glaucous Gull is often seen in the Girdleness area between January and April, sometimes standing about the rubbish tips of Tullos in company with the much more abundant Herring Gulls. A rarer and very similar gull which is also sometimes seen here is the Iceland Gull. These are both fairly regular visitors to northern shores, but the third of a trio of Arctic gulls, the Ivory Gull, is a rarity of the first order. It is an exquisite little pure-white gull, properly belonging to the desolate pack-ice regions of the far north. One might expect its rare visits to Scottish shores to be made in suitable style, on the wings of a blizzard, say, or perched on the tip of an ice-berg. The Ivory Gull seen most recently in Aberdeen was not so minded: it was spotted on the lawn of a suburban back-garden, feeding on bread crusts!

The spring and autumn passage produces a regular crop of rare song birds particularly at Girdleness. The most extraordinary series of such 'falls' of passage migrants ever recorded, took place during a week of appalling weather in early October, 1979. Ninety two millimetres of rain, accompanied by strong gales, fell on October 4th alone, and unprecedented numbers of small birds were literally blown out of the sky. Few birdwatchers who braved the weather will readily forget the rich harvest of birds that week, on the coastline around Girdleness Lighthouse. Among vast numbers of regular migrants were unfamiliar birds like Yellow-browed Warbler, Radde's Warbler, Red-breasted Flycatcher and Scarlet Rosefinch. This forsaken hoard of helpless small birds attracted, in turn, an influx of falcons and sparrowhawks in search of easy pickings. As a fitting climax to the season, there appeared, on October 17th, what is perhaps the rarest bird ever recorded from the north east: an Isabelline Wheatear, far adrift from its native haunts in the steppes of central Asia. The Isabelline Wheatear attracted the attention of the press as well as every birdwatcher in Aberdeen, and it became a local celebrity and a discussion point in public bars, before its disappearance a few days later, with a ring around one of its legs.

Scale : 1 : 25000

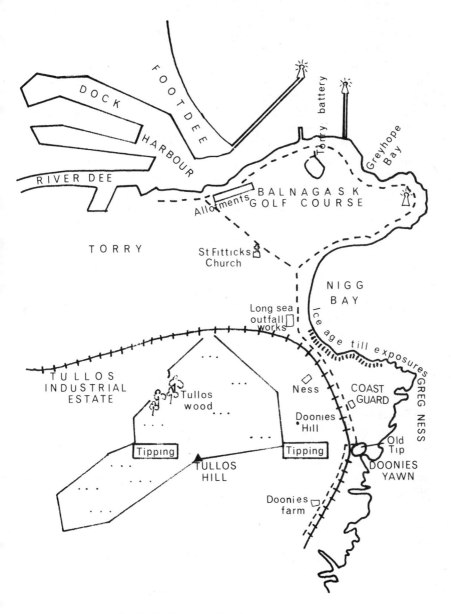

Fig. 11. Girdleness and Environs.

The occurence of such infrequent visitors are more the product of a chance wind, or a serious navigational error on the part of the bird, than any genuine 'desire' to reach our shores. Perhaps the best local example of such a miscalculation was the Lesser Grey Shrike which was found dead at the base of a chimney in Footdee, in September 1952. As chance had it, this central European species had been ringed in Northumberland only a day or two before. The unfortunate Shrike, which ought to have flown south instead of north, has become a classic example of a bird which, already hopelessly off-course, failed to re-orientate itself. Its remains were stuffed and it now perches inside a glass case in the University Museum. That so rare a species was both ringed *and* recovered is almost as notable an event as the bird itself.

There appears to have been more deliberation behind the 'irruptions' of the Pallas' Sand Grouse in the late nineteenth century. This bird, which shares the Asian plains with the Isabelline Wheatbear, was first recorded on the sandhills near Aberdeen in the summer of 1863, when 'many were shot.' Twenty five years later, in 1888, a major irruption resulted in the arrival of 'vast numbers' along the whole coast between Donmouth and the Loch of Strathbeg, and at least one pair bred on what were then extensive dunes at Culbin. After a second successful season in 1889, the Pallas' Sand Grouse suddenly ceased to visit Britain, and hardly a bird has been seen this century.

So much for the more notable visitors from across the seas. Let us now take a closer look at what they find when they arrive.

GIRDLENESS

The headland of Girdleness is one of the 'classic' birdwatching localities of Scotland, both for sea watching and for its regular landfalls of passage migrants. If fate had thrust this promontory of granitic gneiss a mile further out into the North Sea, it would have 'scooped' even more migrating birds and would then rank as one of Britain's major birdwatching headlands. Because of its small size, however, Girdleness misses much of the sea passage, unless strong winds physically blow the birds ashore. In common with almost every other aspect of Aberdeen's wild life, it is its proximity to urban mankind as well as to wild birds, that makes Girdleness such an important area. Any Aberdonian can walk up to Girdleness, spot a Long-tailed Skua or Sooty Shearwater over the ocean, or an Ortolan Bunting among the allotments, and return, for a celebratory pint of beer in a harbour pub, all in the space of a work-day lunch hour. That facility is almost unique to Aberdeen.

The general appearance of Girdleness changed radically in the early 1970s and, from the point of view of bird watchers and migrant birds alike, not for the better. Indeed, for those who remember Girdleness in its prime, the Greyhope Road has become a *Via dolorosa*. At one time, the headland was full of 'untidy' patches of scrub and long grass, old walls and piles of rubble, all hated by golfers and the City bureaucracy, but much favoured by migratory birds. When the Council got to work on the area in the early 1970s, a major tidying up operation soon reduced the available rough cover to a fraction of its former area. If one braves the flying golf balls and manic drivers and walks around the headland today, it soon becomes apparent that Girdleness is not what it was.

If we begin our outward journey from the harbour, the first important locality we reach is the Council allotments. These used to be divided up by turf banks, which provided excellent shelter for the birds, whilst the broken ground in between provided forage for seed-eating and insect-eating birds. Unfortunately, whilst the turf banks protected the crops from gales, they failed to protect them from urban vandals. The Council's solution was to pull down the old turf walls and replace them with a black chain-link fence. This kept out the vandals, but failed to protect the crops from gales and the unhappy allotment holders have been reduced to putting up their own makeshift fences of driftwood and corrugated iron. The birds have not found the change to their liking.

A little further up the road lies Torry Battery. These walls, with their seaward-facing turrets, were built in 1860 to repel an imaginary invasion. When the power-that-be finally decided, in the 1950s, that Scotland was not going to be invaded via Aberdeen after all, the Battery was demolished. Its rubble-filled ruins were in exactly the right place to attract small migratory birds, particularly the Black Redstart. 'It crawled with birds,' say those who remember it in its great years. But a rubble-filled ruin is a bête noire to a city which prides itself on tidy, well-maintained lawns and flower beds. The Battery commands a fine view of the harbour, and in the early seventies, the City Parks Department set about turning it into 'an amenity'. The rubble was removed and replaced with a neat sward of sown grass with cobblestone edging and a central flagstaff. Parking bays with 'recreation furniture' were carved into the slopes on either side, and only a few patches of 'rough' escaped the mower. The Battery now looks very tidy indeed, except for the litter, but rather sterile. Migrant birds are sometimes seen nearby, sitting in the gullies for lack of anywhere else to go.

Greyhope Bay, a little further on, is still the resort of sea-ducks and Kittiwakes, but its landward margins have been all but obliterated. Above the storm beach there was once a wet area with sedges, willows and small pools. Most of this was buried by fill in order to protect the road from coastal erosion, whilst the western side of the bay is masked from view by a wooden fence, and used to store granite setts.

Rounding the well known Girdleness lighthouse, erected in 1833 by the Commissioners of the Northern Lights, we look down over Nigg Bay. Standing alone in the midst of a relentless green sward lies St Fittick's Church, which looks as lonely and incongruous as a dolls house on a snooker table. When Aberdeen City was a safe distance away, this old ruin was surrounded by patches of whins, willow-herb and rubbly walls, all of which provided cover for birds alighting from Nigg Bay. When these were swept away by the City's improvement scheme, the Scottish Ornithologist's Club felt moved to complain to the Council. They were told: 'never mind, we'll plant something there for you'. The 'something' turned out to be rows of small sapling trees, each consisting of a straight pole with about three leaves on top. The trees failed to attract the interest of any bird, and most quickly succumbed to the climate or vandals. Many people, including myself, see the area around St Fittick's as one of the least imaginative parts of Aberdeen: a green desert with rubbish tipping on one side and the nastier type of modern housing on the other. This is the view of Aberdeen which first greets anyone travelling in on the north bound train.

It could be argued that none of this matters, that all the birds have to do is fly just a little further inland and they would find all the food and cover they need. Dr Alan Knox, the ornithological recorder for Aberdeenshire, disagrees. The migrant birds, he argues, are under great stress when they arrive on shore, often simply blown out of the air. They are literally on their last legs, and need immediate shelter to recuperate. Furthermore, a large 'fall' of small birds inevitably attracts their predators - the raptors, large gulls and owls. In the open, on the naked turf, they are sitting ducks, or to be more accurate, crouching song birds. The City's tidying up policy has almost certainly increased the rate of mortality of small birds, although, as Alan Knox acknowledges, this would not be an easy thing to *prove*.

A City official could, with some justice, point to the acres of dense whin scrub on nearby Tullos hill. What cover can little patches of coastal scrub and turf walls offer compared with *that*? And it has to be admitted that rather few birdwatchers visit Tullos Hill: even if the scrub there was full of tired birds, keeping their heads down, it would be almost impossible to see them. This would be in their favour: a hidden bird is a safe bird, a visible bird is a bird at risk. But a scrubland full of invisible birds would not be of great interest for our hypothetical office worker who want to *see* birds. The conservation purist might argue that this is irrelevant, but urban conservation is about people as well as wildlife and Girdleness loses much of its uniqueness if the human side of the equation is omitted. The policies of the municipal authorities may or may not be having a serious effect on the birds, but by removing isolated patches of 'untidiness', where the migrants concentrate in numbers, they are threatening our chances of seeing them.

Against the general trend, one small area has become increasingly attractive to birds. The field behind the pre-fabs and construction gear at Nigg Bay has become wetter of late, and passage waders such as Jack Snipe and Green Sandpiper have taken to visiting the area. The reason for the subsidence of this field is not difficult to surmise: underneath the grass lies an old rubbish tip. Collectors of bottles and other antique rubbish are helping things along by digging holes, which immediately flood with water.

Elsewhere on the headland and down by Nigg Bay, the short grass of Balnagask golf course reigns almost supreme. This is very bad news for skylarks, birds which must give incalculable pleasure to many, and not only birdwatchers, but which require level areas of tall grass in which to nest. The few patches of whin scrub remaining at Girdleness continue to be whittled away by a slow process of attrition and, at the present rate, it will soon be as bare as a skull. There is an increasingly urgent need to somehow convince local Councillors that the birds of Girdleness headland are part of its amenity; that Aberdeen's several hundred serious birdwatchers need places to see birds in the same way that a footballer needs a football pitch.

DONMOUTH

Whereas Girdleness excels in migratory song-birds, Donmouth is wader country. The sandhills and grazing marsh around Donmouth, long ago underwent the indignities described so vividly in Trail's flora (see Chapter Two). However, grassland lying on top of a thick stratum of domestic rubbish is liable to subsidence, and, over the years, this has resulted in a series of surface depressions, which contain standing water in wet weather. This area has developed into a wonderful area to see wading birds at high tide, when their usual feeding areas on the estuarine mud is covered by water. The autumn passage between August and November provides a concentration of almost every wader regularly seen in the north east. Dunlin, Bar-tailed Godwit, Redshank, Knot, Ruff, Curlew Sandpiper, Little Stint, Turnstone, Ringed Plover, Golden Plover, Lapwing and Oystercatcher are the more or less regular visitors, but there is a good chance of seeing rarities such as Pectoral Sandpiper, Temminck's Stint and Red-necked Phalarope. This is an extraordinary assemblage to find within a mile of the centre of Europe's oil capital, and it is by no means an exhaustive list. As an added bonus, there were, until quite recently, a series of small hummocks and pools nearby, which were used by wild duck and large flocks of finches.

Every bird using this area is threatened with disturbance from golf balls, dogs and holidaymakers, but their very habitat is now under threat. As with Girdleness, so too with Donmouth: municipal 'tidying up' operations have taken place, with varying degrees of success. The hummocks and pools were easy bait; they were drained and levelled until the surface was as flat as a pancake, and only roosting gulls show much interest in it now. Both banks of the river Don below the bridge were landscaped, and much of their rough scrub and willow-herb was replaced by strident yellow armies of the pernicious daffodil. On the credit side, the authorities have planted some willow bushes and a bank of rough vegetation has been left above the estuary.

The subsidence pools have been more persistent devils to deal with. For seven years they have defied attempts to drain them, on safety grounds, including the less than subtle excavations of a mechanical digger. So deep did this machine dig that it began to unearth the rubbish lying underneath the topsoil and the neat bowling green turf. This discovery brought in the bottle collectors, last mentioned digging holes at Nigg Bay, rushing to the spot in search of loot. Trail's lament for the lost sandhills, written over sixty years ago, thus takes on an exquisite irony:

> 'the rubbish employed in these operations (the dumping of refuse over the dunes) may in some distant period afford relics to some ardent antiquarian exploring the ruins of Aberdeen, though I fear his prizes would represent our present civilisation in but a sordid light'.

I would give a lot to hear Trail's comments on some of the present goings-on at Kings Links.

INSECT MIGRATION AT ABERDEEN

Isabelline Wheatears excite multitudes but migratory insects arrive and depart un-noticed except by a handful of entomologists. The immigrant butterflies and hawkmoths are a partial exception and are usually large and colourful enough to draw attention to themselves, particularly since they often take up suburban habits, visiting gardens and feasting on exotic flowers.

The last half-decade has seen two notable years for migratory butterflies. Oddly enough, the more spectacular was during the cold wet summer and early autumn of 1980, in which the north eastern coast was invaded by three separate waves of Painted Lady butterflies. I was lucky enough to witness the first of these, when immaculate Painted

Ladies started flying inland from over the North Sea. They were flying strongly and purposefully, without the usual dalliance of a butterfly; it was as if they knew where they were going. Reaching land, they alighted on the rocks and bare soil above the sea and clung there motionless, with their beautiful tawny wings outstretched: one could almost imagine them panting. The first wave in early June was followed by a second at the end of July, but the greatest influx was reserved for the autumn. On September 28th, anyone in the vicinity of Nigg Bay would have had an unforgettable day as many hundreds of representatives of a new generation of Painted Ladies poured in from the sea, accompanied by smaller numbers of that more regular visitor, the Red Admiral. Among them was a Clouded Yellow, the first recorded specimen seen in the north east since 1941. These are all thought to be Scandinavian butterflies which were flying south, but had been blown off-course by some quirk in the weather.

1980 saw the largest numbers of Painted Ladies ever recorded in the north east, and they briefly became an everyday sight on Aberdeen's wasteland Buddleia bushes. Some must have laid eggs on their food-plant, the thistle, but neither their caterpillars nor the adult butterflies are known to survive normal British winters, let alone Aberdeen's icy blasts. To that extent, their sudden, unexplained Odysseys are quite pointless.

That glorious dry summer of 1976 brought an unusually high influx of Scandinavian immigrants to Aberdeen, although the mass invasions one remembers from that year are not the butterflies but the ladybirds. Dr Mark Young, lecturer in entomology at the university, was kept busy with frequent requests to identify this or that unheard-of insect. Many of these were in fact common species, and when he was asked to identify an 'enormous' moth caught at Ellon, and imprisoned in a shoe-box, he was not unduly excited. Expecting to see a Yellow Underwing or some other common large moth, he casually removed the box lid. Out shot a moth the size of a small bat, which made straight for the window. Fortunately it was closed, and the astonished witnessses were able to feast their eyes on a live Blue Underwing, that nonpareil of British moths and very rare indeed in the north of Scotland. A similar SOS came in from Garthdee Hotel, where the catering staff assembled to watch Mark Young unearth a huge and splendid Convolvulus Hawkmoth from underneath a tumbler.

Two other large and extremely rare visitors are the Camberwell Beauty butterfly and the Death's-head Hawkmoth. Both have been found in trawl boats, and in the case of the Camberwell Beauty, among cargoes of timber from Scandinavia. This has given rise to the specul-

Chapter 9

Three Fragments

In this chapter, I have chosen three areas near Aberdeen to examine in rather more depth than has been possible in the preceding part of this book. Each of these is an area of considerable local value, and their respective histories cast an interesting light on municipal attitudes to planning and the natural landscape. For two out of these three fragments, the facts of their case-histories are neither happy nor particularly edifying, but they do, I hope, illustrate some of the pitfalls which can overtake men of genuine good-will, when they attempt to put an idea into practice through the paper jungle world of contemporary local government. For those whom my remarks will inevitably offend, I should emphasise that I am not seeking to impugn their motives nor to apportion blame, only to try to establish the reason why these events happened in the way they did.

I. LOIRSTON COUNTRY PARK

The Grampians reach their last gasp on the southern marches of Aberdeen, as they tumble down from the heathery ridges of Kincorth, Tullos and Doonies Hill to the blue ribbon of the Dee and the coastal headlands of Girdle Ness and Greg Ness. This area, known by Aberdonians as 'the Gramps', has defied the efforts of several centuries to 'improve' it. The cold, salt-laden winds of the North Sea have kept the ridge inviolate as the last of the 'barren wastes' at Aberdeen's door.

> 'High upon 'the Grampians'
> the wins blaw sweet an' free;
> tang o' the sea fae Girdleness
> like incense wafts tae me,'

sang the muse of one Bon Accord ballad and many similar refrains have been written. It was here, on the old pack horse route over Tullos Hill, that the early traveller looked down over Aberdeen and sighed with relief at the sight of his journey's end. Most of those pre-improvement

era travellers who have left us their impressions complained bitterly
about the quality of the road and the desolation of its surroundings.
Time has changed all that. The maligned 'Gramps' have for many years
been a popular walking and picnic area, and, more recently, the chief
bone of contention in an unusually controversial Country Park.

The human and natural history of the Gramps are rich with interest.
Their most notable feature is the Bronze Age cairn cemetary on and
around the top of Tullos Hill, which consists of four round cairns,
respectively named Cat Cairn, Baron's Cairn, Tullos Cairn and Crab's
Cairn. They are all prominent mounds of stones between forty and sixty
feet across and between six and eight feet high, and each has been
scheduled as an ancient monument. They have never been excavated
but they probably date from 2500 to 1500 BC and contain funeral urns
and a number of 'cist' burials - stone-lined graves, each containing a
body laid on its side in a crouched attitude, and accompanied by a pot.
Although cairns of similar size are not uncommon in the north east, it is
exceptional to find a group of them close together, as at Tullos; nor are
they, in all probability, the only features of interest to archaeologists,for
the Scottish Development Department (Ancient Monuments) consider
that other less prominent prehistoric sites may also exist on the hill.

Until 1970, Tullos Hill was a piece of unreclaimable land, just outside
the city limits. Local tradition has it that there was once a lepers' colony
nearby, and at the foot of the hill there was a medieval watering place,
St Jacob's Well, now preserved in the Winter Gardens at Duthie Park.
Troops were billeted here in Nissen huts during Hitler's War, and they
wiled away their boredom by damaging all four cairns. Otherwise the
area was left to the elements, except for some desultory rough grazing,
chicken farms and dog kennels. Its main asset, so far as the general
public are concerned, is that it provides a viewpoint with magnificent
vistas of Aberdeen.

Tullos and Kincorth Hills were both regarded as among the best
localities near the city by Aberdonian naturalists in late Victorian times.
One contemporary report mentions that Oak Fern, Sundew, Bog Asph-
odel, Lesser Twayblade and 'several of our wild orchids' could be found
on Tullos. Professor Charles Gimingham, visiting the same site during
its years of decline in 1976, regarded it as still 'of considerable ecological
interest and value, in view of the range of plant species and communities
represented so close to Aberdeen'. These included stands of heather
which vary in age because of periodic accidental fires, and associated
heathland plants like blaeberry, Bell Heather, Chickweed Wintergreen
and a good variety of mosses and lichens. The dry heath grades into
wet hollows, the largest of which is very wet, even in summer, and is

covered by Cotton-grass, Cross-leaved Heath, Heath Spotted Orchid, Crowberry, and hummocks of *Sphagum* moss with open peat pools. The eastern side of Tullos Hill is a mass of gravelly mounds and ridges, originating from the river-born sands and gravels of the late Ice Age. The hollows in between are waterlogged, and lined with peat. Several very similar areas of hummock and hollow occurred near Aberdeen in the seventeenth century, but Tullos is the only one which has survived.

The appearance of the vegetation may have changed in two ways, during the past century. Maps of 1860 indicate that the leeward side of Tullos Hill contained mixed woodland, probably of planted origin, most of which has since disappeared. Secondly, in common with many other hills near Aberdeen, Tullos has a much denser covering of whin scrub than of old. The reason for this is a matter for dispute; possibly the decline of rough grazing by domestic animals, or a cessation of controlled muirburn, may have had something to do with it.

Such, then, is the area which, together with Kincorth Hill and the rocky coast, forms the greater part of Loirston Country Park. There is clearly a potential here for an amenity which most British cities could but envy. The views of Aberdeen are dramatic, access is not a problem, the scenery and wildlife are diverse and interesting. Moreover the area lies within Aberdeen's Green Belt and is protected from development. When the idea of designating this area as a Country Park was first mooted in 1970, the City's plans were nothing if not ambitious: walkers, riders, golfers, birdwatchers, picnickers and boat people, all were to be catered for. The local farms would be 'encouraged' to remain in active use 'to preserve the country atmosphere', and a museum and Information Centre were to be set up, providing displays of country crafts, farm implements and details of the natural history and archaeology of Loirston. Much of the original report shows uneasy signs of the urban planner's touch. A typical example is the statement that 'the traditional picnic can sometimes be an uncomfortable experience'. 'A much more civilised note', the report went on, could be struck by the provision of 'recreation furniture' of a 'suitably rural design'. The most ambitious scheme of all was to stock the fields with breeds of ponies, cattle and sheep. 'Some breeds of wild animals' were to be encouraged to roam in these fields, including, according to the report, squirrels. In short, the park was to be a townsman's Arcadia, a countryside tamed and modified for mass enjoyment.

The best laid schemes o' mice an' men gang aft agley. In the case of Loirston, it soon became apparent that the paper plan would be difficult to transform into reality. For one thing, the owners of the two largest farms within the proposed park were not much interested in seeing their properties turned into outdoor museums. For another, a large and vital chunk of the park on Tullos Hill was already used by the City Cleansing Department for dumping domestic and industrial rubbish. The dichotomy between the use of the hill for rubbish dumping by one City Department and its role as a tranquil rural haven for city folk under another is the key issue which continues to bedevil Loirston Country Park, and which makes a mockery of its avowed aims. Let us, therefore, home in on Tullos Hill, not the pre-1970 wild heath we have thus far described, but the town tip of subsequent years.

Like, I suspect, most people who have set foot on Tullos Hill in the past ten years, I have vivid memories of my first visit. I did at least have some warning, for my friend Malcolm Smith had gone there the week before and had written a report about it. His stunned reaction to what he saw there must speak for many Aberdonians:

> 'I still have some regard for an old boyhood playground of mine when there were nothing but farms and the kirk between the Dee and the hilltop... If you've never seen the area before, you are warned. I should have been prepared after seeing the endless lines of lorries coming up the Nigg brae to deposit their muck (our muck) south of Ness, but over the top to Barons Cairns sickened me with its flat expanse of pulverised rubbish and shredded plastic everywhere.'

A hillside which receives over eight hundred tonnes of pulverised rubbish every week is, to say the least, not exactly an asset for a Country Park. But the phased programme of tipping at Tullos began well before anyone had entertained plans for public outdoor recreation at this site. Moreover, when planning permission was sought for a pulverisation plant and tipping ground in 1968, nobody saw fit to file an objection. Indeed, from some points of view, Tullos was a logical choice of site. In the mid sixties, there was an urgent need to find a suitable place where most of Aberdeen's rapidly increasing tonnage of domestic refuse could be dumped. The first site which inevitably occured to everyone was Rubislaw Quarry: that vast excavation would see out Aberdeen's rubbish problem for the rest of the century. Unfortunately there were two snags. Firstly, the quarry was in active use at that time and the operators assured the Council that it would remain so for many years to come. No one then foresaw that the quarry would be forced by flooding, to close less than two years after this optimistic forecast. The second snag was that Rubislaw Quarry lies in the heart of a residential area - and an exclusive and up-market one at that. Any attempt to impose a noisy and probably smelly refuse plant and tip in such surroundings, would meet with stiff resistance and Councils do not usually relish head-on collisions. There was no alternative quarry site which was both large enough and sufficiently accessible; indeed most disused quarries near Aberdeen had already been filled. It was with some desperation, therefore, that the eyes of the Council turned southwards to a large patch of ground which they already owned, where no one lived and for which nobody had any definite plans: Tullos Hill. Planning permission was sought and obtained and, in 1968, work began on a pulverisation plant below the slopes of the hill. The machinery ground into action in 1970, and shortly afterwards the first lorries began to trundle up the slope with their sinister loads of pulverised waste.

The pulverisation plant has an expected industrial life of twenty five years, and the Cleansing Department's intention was to implement a phased programme of tipping at Tullos over that period. When any tip reached capacity, it would be contoured and reclaimed, and a new tip would form elsewhere on the hill. The hill itself would receive pulverised domestic refuse only; 'crude' industrial waste and oil sludges would be deposited downslope around the site of Ness farm.

One wonders, however, whether the implications of this form of tipping on a windy hillside overlooking a city, had been fully thought out. That the tips would be unusually prominent was obvious. 'Out of sight, out of mind', the usual law governing where a city's waste products are dumped was patently broken in this case, but there seemed at first to be little serious public concern. However, two factors which may not have been apparent at the time, have since given cause for alarm. The first concerns wind-blown debris. The pulverisation process breaks down about half of the domestic waste, but some, consisting mostly of plastics and metals, remains partially intact. Since nobody thought fit to cover or fence in the tips, numberless grimy shreds of plastic now whirl up into the air every time the wind blows and are scattered about the hill, where they become caught up on the thorns of the whin bushes. And since the plastic is non-biodegradable, there it stays. The nearby railway cutting acts as a natural wind tunnel, and a passenger on the incoming train from Dundee often knew he was nearing the City of Granite and Roses when he noticed the blizzard of black plastic blowing around the carriage.

That, heaven knows, is a bad enough advertisement for a city which is so proud of its appearance, but another aspect of hillside tipping has appeared more recently, which has even more serious implications. A large tip looks, externally at least, sterile and inert, apart from the umbrella of gulls screaming overhead. Inside, however, it is warm and seething with chemical change. As the tip material decomposes, soluble materials begin to be leached out by rainwater. This leachate is acidic, and in a later stage of decomposition, it may contain the salts of heavy metals in solution. Since the tips lie on a hill-top, the natural path for the leachate to take is downwards into the wet hollows and, ultimately, into the Industrial Estate below. The leachate is white, slimy and foul-smelling. The most poignant image of the damage inflicted to Tullos Hill's wildlife that I know of was witnessed in March 1981 by Pam Ritchie, a former Countryside Ranger: a little frog was trying to struggle through the white slime running into the hollow; already it was barely able to move and would shortly be overwhelmed. For those millions who rejoice in Kermit and the Muppets, that is, perhaps, not a pleasant sight. There is, indeed, evidence that this white slime is at least toxic enough to cause damage to some sturdy beech trees, and it has now entered, via a ditch, a field within the boundary of the Industrial Estate.

The organs which, next to the eyes, are most assailed by the horrors of Tullos Hill are the nose, and, for some at least, the stomach. But the evil reputation of the tips is, in this respect, largely undeserved. Decomposing pulverised refuse gives off a variety of gases such as carbon dioxide and ammonia, but although the resultant odour is rather musty, like a dusty attic, and vaguely offensive, it is within the limits of human endurance. The really nasty fumes of Tullos Hill issue not from the tips or even the pulverising plant, but from a fish meal factory on the Industrial Estate. This factory has recently had a filtering system installed and it is hoped that this will prevent the worst of the smell.

In 1978, Derek Lovejoy and Partners, an Edinburgh firm of planning and landscape consultants, were jointly commissioned by the Scottish Development Agency and Aberdeen District Council to produce recommendations for the reinstatement and future use of Tullos Hill, and to make an assessment of the likely impact of future tipping. Their report, which went before the District Council joint committee in March 1981, recommended that tipping should cease on Tullos Hill altogether, 'at the earliest possible time', and that operations should be transferred to the site of Ness Farm, below the hill. They also strongly suggested that a number of controls should be introduced to safeguard the damaging side-effects of the hillside tips. The controls include limiting the area of active tipping, stockpiling the underlying soil of new tip sites, erecting a fence around each tip, and introducing a drainage system to control the flow of leachates. The Lovejoy Report also looked further ahead to the day if and when Tullos Hill becomes a part of Loirston Country Park which people will once again want to visit. They recommended that the tip sites and the leeward hill slopes should be re-afforested and were cautiously optimistic that this was possible -

although, as many who have tried to grow trees near Aberdeen's coast will testify, their establishment is not easy.

This was the basis of the package of proposals which were delivered to Aberdeen District Council in 1981. The Leisure and Recreation Department, supported by the planners, wanted the provisions of the report to be accepted. The Cleansing Department, on the other hand, pointed out that the alternative site at Ness Farm simply could not accomodate the expected production of pulverised refuse of the next fifteen years without drastic changes in technique. The stuff had to be tipped *somewhere*. The argument boiled down to one of cost: if tipping was to cease on Tullos Hill, the volume of tipped refuse must be reduced. There are several ways of doing this: it could take the form of a baling plant, which compresses pulverised refuse into solid blocks, or the installation of an incinerator, or even some advanced technology device which could recycle methane gas for industrial use. Any of these options would cost up to several millions of pounds to implement, and raise the per capita cost of tipping from £9 at present (one of the cheapest urban rates in Scotland) to nearer £20 (one of the most expensive). The Council's discussion about the future of Tullos concentrated on the more immediate future. A Conservative Councillor's proposal to carry on regardless at Tullos, excluding only a wet hollow 'in accordance of the wishes of conservationists', was defeated *by only one vote*. The proposal which carried the day was to defer any decision, pending more detailed reports. Some Councillors appear to hold the view that an open sewer which is in the process of leaking back into the city is objectionable only to a few 'conservationists' and, even then, solely on the grounds of its damage to wildlife. The potential damage which the effects of unlimited tipping might have on *people* does not seem to have occurred to them.

Fortunately, not everyone shares such a limited view. Any decision which the Council may make on the future of the hill will have to take into account the Scottish Development Agency's refusal to grant-aid any further reclamation of the tips, unless the Lovejoy report's recommendations are accepted. The Countryside Commission for Scotland and the local press have lent their backing to the proposals of the report, and the former have taken the unprecedented step of removing Loirston from their list of 'officially recognised' country parks, since it does not match the criteria expected of one. These are hard blows to Aberdeen's prestige and for that reason, if for no other, the City will probably eventually decide in favour of discontinuing the tipping on Tullos Hill.

Ironically, if one considers wildlife in isolation, the best possible outcome would be if the tips were *not* reclaimed. Rubbish tips often

become rich hunting grounds for plants and insects, and they have the
additional attraction that one never knows exactly what one is going to
find. Of course the docks, umbellifers and willow-herbs which colonise
the tip are quite different from the natural vegetation of the hill. The
original Country Park report stated rather glibly that the tipped ground
'will be restored to natural contours and vegetation'. This is probably
impossible; at the least it would be prohibitively expensive. What is
much more likely to happen is that the old tips will be smoothed over,
sown with grass and planted with bulbs. If so, the wildlife of the tip
and the wildlife of the heath will both disappear, and Tullos Hill will
become another part of the grass desert stretching south of Girdleness.

This highlights a second aspect of Loirston Country Park: that of the
apparently ambivalent attitude by the Parks managers towards wilderness and nature. Perhaps this comes across most vividly when one
compares the descriptions in the official guide to the Park with what
one sees on the ground. Wildlife is one of the principle topics of this
booklet, and its pages include many rather impressionistic drawings of
flowers, birds and mammals. The passages describing the wildlife are of
an affectionate if slightly treacly nature: the Wryneck, for instance, is a
'funny little bird' (not that any visitor to the park is likely to see one);
the Cormorant is an 'ugly-looking fellow'. This is harmless enough stuff.
What I find more remarkable is not what the booklet says, but what it
doesn't say. There is no mention at all of the rubbish tips on Tullos Hill,
although they are one of the most prominent features of the park and
surely one which visitors would want information about. Torry Battery
is recommended by the author of the booklet as a good place to see
migratory birds, despite the fact that his Department stripped that
classic locality of most of its attraction for birds during the wholesale
'cleaning up' of this area in the seventies. The overall impression one
gets is that we, the public, are intended to believe that everything is
for the best in this best of all possible parks. The darker side of reality
is expunged from its pages.

The reality, alas, is that Loirston Country Park is scarcely worthy of
the name. Far from the initial grandiose scheme of 1970, the only visible benefits accruing from its designation are improved footpaths along
the coastline and Kincorth Hill, and the creation of an open farm at the
old steading of Doonies. Doonies provides the visitor with an unlabelled
display of local agricultural implements, and an assortment of farm
animals (plus, for some reason, a Llama). The open fields around the
farm house are enclosed by rather nasty chain-link fences, perhaps in
deference to a warning in the original report that the park's beauty spots
'be protected from becoming victims of their own beauty'. The farm is

Fig. 12. The approaches to Tullos Hill. One of the recently levelled rubbish tips lies to the right of the path, and the spread of windblown plastics is all too apparent.

Fig. 13. Scotstown Moor 1981, with road construction in progress. New housing estates throng the western horizon, and gorse thickets have invaded what was once open heather muir.

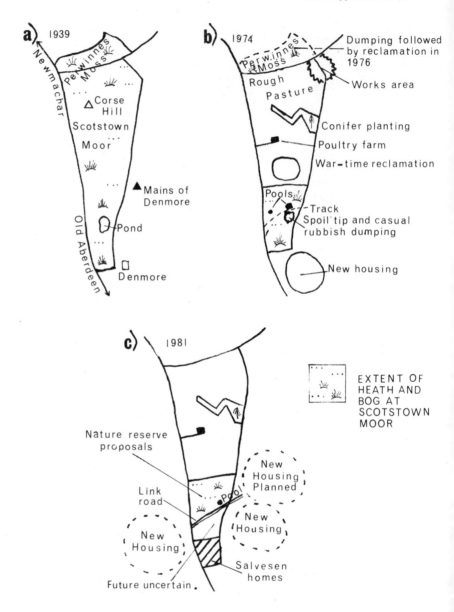

Scale : approx. 1 : 25000

a) 1939

Newmachar

Perwinnes Moss

△ Corse Hill

Scotstown

Moor

▲ Mains of Denmore

Pond

Old Aberdeen

▢ Denmore

b) 1974

Perwinnes Moss

Rough Pasture

Dumping followed by reclamation in 1976

Works area

Conifer planting

Poultry farm

War-time reclamation

Pools

Track

Spoil tip and casual rubbish dumping

New housing

c) 1981

Nature reserve proposals

Link road

New Housing

Future uncertain.

New Housing Planned

New Housing

Salvesen homes

Pool

EXTENT OF HEATH AND BOG AT SCOTSTOWN MOOR

Fig. 14. The decline and fall of Scotstown Moor 1939 - 1981.

a well-meaning attempt at what has become known as 'interpretation', but it proves, at least to myself, that urban designs on countryside realities usually fall short of their aims. This might be an appropriate epitaph for Loirston Country Park as a whole.

SCOTSTOWN MOOR

When the first botanical records for Aberdeen were being gathered in the late eighteenth century, the once extensive heaths and bogs of the parish had already been split into fragments by the great land rush of the Age of Improvement. Three of those surviving fragments of heath appear again and again in the early floras: Ferryhill Moss, Stocket Moor and Scotstown (or Scotston) Moor. The first two lay at the gates of the expanding burgh, and, as we have seen, both were soon buried under housing.. Scotstown Moor was further away from the city, in the heart of the country parish of Old Machar. It lay within easy walking distance of Kings College and, from the 1830s onwards, was regularly visited by university botany classes. By 1870, it was perhaps the most famous botanical locality near Aberdeen and was the subject of an early natural history monograph by John Sim. The locality encompassed two separate areas of bog, linked by a square mile or so of dry heath, rising to two hundred and eighty feet above sea level on the summit of Corse Hill.

Scotstown Moor's botanical riches are almost legendary, and therefore, perhaps, easily overstated. Over two hundred and fifty species of flowering plants are recorded, many of which would once have been common in the neighbourhood of Aberdeen, but are now confined to the small remaining enclaves of unreclaimed heath and undrained marsh. Scotstown Moor was different from most heaths in the area in that surface 'flushes' of water containing dissolved lime and other minerals, drained downhill into the bogs, enriching the soils and allowing several lime-loving plants, rare in Aberdeen District, to flourish. These included Grass of Parnassus, Hairy Stonecrop, Least Clubmoss, Fen Bedstraw and the only known patch of Black Bog-rush in the north eastern lowlands. Peaty pools near the centre of the basin-shaped bogs contained semi-aquatic plants such as Mares Tail, Shore-weed, Small Bur-reed and Bogbean. These pools and the mosses around them were also unusually rich in insect-eating plants: at least two species of Bladderwort, which sometimes excelled themselves by flowering, something they rarely do in Scotland; two species of Sundew, including the only place near Aberdeen where the handsome Greater Sundew could be found, and an abundance of Butterwort. Nearby, under the shade of a plantation of pines and fine beech trees, was a famous (perhaps too famous) locality for Twinflower, which rubbed shoulders with two other north eastern specialities, the Intermediate Wintergreen and that charming white orchid, the Creeping Ladies Tresses. This is by no means a complete list but it might serve to indicate why botanists from the university and local natural history societies regarded the moor as something of a Shangri-la. The fauna of the moor was regarded as more orthodox, although insect collectors in particular found much to interest them. Readers may recall that Scotstown Moor was the arena of the great Marsh Moth Mystery.

But the appeal of Scotstown Moor went beyond its interest for local naturalists. The moor was a Commonty, a system of land tenure which had undoubtedly preserved it from early enclosure and reclamation. Alexander Walker, in a strident piece of pamphleteering called *The Commonty of Perwinnes* (1893), gave the popular view that the moor was the heritage of the people:

> 'a magnificent stretch of land, a city's noble dower, a Commonty, a very garden of delights to every lover of nature, has passed into possession of the City of Aberdeen by its union and absorption with the old Episcopal Burgh ... It has not been kept as it is without a struggle. It has been coveted by neighbouring lairds and *sans doute*, could each of them have proven how much was his, it would have been parcelled out and divided long ago... The people of Aberdeen have still a grand possession there, and it will be their own fault if one other road of it is lost'.

Three years later J W Davidson, the then Depute Town Clerk, wrote a more sober account, *The Common Moss and Freedom-hill of Old Aberdeen*. He made it clear that although Scotstown Moor was a Commonty, it was the property of the Bishopric of Aberdeen, and farmed by the proprietor of Perwinnes. The feuars of Old Aberdeen were granted certain rights by the Episcopacy, notably the right of common grazing and divot (sod cutting) on Corse Hill, and peat cutting from Perwinnes Moss. The general public were customarily afforded free access. This was a survivor of the old system of feal and servitude, and geared to farming practices long since outmoded. Such time-honoured but legally fragile customs tend to melt away under the pressures of the modern world, and this is more or less what happened to Scotstown Moor.

The moor and its mosses survived the nineteenth century intact. The literature of the early 1900s is full of references to happy botanical excursions: '...passing through the wood en route for Scotstown Moor, *Linnaea* was seen to be holding its own ... Lesser Bladderwort in profuse flower ... on the way to the moor some fine specimens of Field Wound-wort'. By the time the Great War had broken out, dark clouds were gathering:

'(The moor is) losing its value as a haunt for natural history collect-ors. Owing no doubt to drainage operations, many plants have disappeared and since the Fresh Air Camp for Children was instit-uted, bird life seems to have had a set back'.

Hitler's War was the occasion of a much more serious set back. The urgent need, because of the German U-boat campaign, to put more land into agricultural production led to the partial reclamation of Corse Hill, at public expense. Intensified cattle grazing was probably respons-ible for the gradual replacement of the heather by grass, and the war-time grazings were afterwards ploughed up and reseeded. This severed the old locality into two independent basin bogs, almost a mile apart. The northern basin, Perwinnes Moss, was the larger but the southern part near Denmore, which is still customarily referred to as Scotstown Moor, was botanically the richer of the two, and retained a good propor-tion of its indigenous flora, although, by this time, about twenty of the rarer species had been lost. This little patch, consisting of about twenty five acres of wet heath, bog and dry scrub-land, was very vulnerable to any changes in the use of the surrounding land. By 1970, its testing time had come.

The decade of the seventies saw the slow decay of Scotstown Moor. Its story is a convoluted one, full of blind alleys, red herrings and 'state-ments of intent' from one body or another, which somehow were never translated into action. I shall attempt to unravel the main strands. From the beginning of the seventies, the very existence of the moor was threatened from two directions. The ownership of the moor had passed into the hands of the tenant of Perwinnes, whose avowed intention was to sell the land for housing or, failing that, to reclaim it in its entirety for agriculture. The local authorities' attitudes to the moor were more complicated. Since 1933, Scotstown Moor had been categorised as a listed open space under the Aberdeen and District Joint Town Planning Scheme. Aberdeen County Council intended to leave it as a 'green wedge' within the new overspill housing schemes planned for this area. The moor was officially labelled as 'wasteland' on the plans, and the Council, who were apparently unaware of its cultural and scientific significance, formulated an Environmental Improvement Scheme to clear away the gorse scrub and afforest the moor. They would have needed the owner's agreement for this of course, but the Council had compulsory purchase powers to fall back on in cases of this sort. In the event, blanket afforestation would have annihilated Scotstown Moor as completely as housing or the plough.

At this stage, a third party joined the fray. In 1972, the scientific value of Scotstown Moor reached the attention of the Nature Conservancy, who scheduled the moor as a Site of Special Scientific Interest as 'a small area of interesting wet heath and valley mire'. To those readers who are not familiar with SSSI designation, this meant that the Nature Conservancy was now given the statutory right to comment on any planning application within the boundaries of the SSSI. The decision whether or not to grant planning permission still rested with the local authority. From a planner's point of view, the notification of a SSSI is the 'official' seal of approval of a site's high worth from a nature conservation standpoint, something which they would consider when coming to their decision. In the case of Scotstown Moor, SSSI designation probably influenced the County Council's decision not to allow any housing development on the site, and to abandon their afforestation scheme. It also influenced the Department of Agriculture's refusal to grant-aid the owner's proposal to drain Scotstown Moor. The larger but 'less interesting' Perwinnes Moss was eventually filled in and drained, however, after a long wrangle in the mid-seventies, and so thoroughly that virtually nothing of it remains. The last tiny fragment of the old Commonty now stood alone.

In the meantime, local Government reorganisation had resulted in the present two tier system of District and Region. The new District of Aberdeen City extended the boundary of the city to include land, such as Scotstown Moor, which had previously been under the control of the County Council, from whom several plans were inherited. One of these, a document called the Aberdeen Area Strategy Plan, included a proposal to set up a Country Park at Old Machar, which would have required the purchase by the Council of what was left of Scotstown Moor. The interplay which follows between Aberdeen City District and Grampian Regional Council, is a tangle which some readers may find tedious. I beg their endurance; its relevance should soon be apparent. The Aberdeen Area Strategy Plan was studied by the Regional Planning committee, who quickly decided not to adopt the plan, but to regard it as 'useful background information' and 'of historic interest'. In the meantime, they proposed that a Working Party of interested bodies be set up 'to critically examine the situation' of the proposed Old Machar Country Park, in order to make 'a policy recommendation for consideration by the relevant local authorities'. The City District thought that this matter was none of the Region's business and refused to attend discussions: 'no useful purpose would be served in participating in the Working Party which the Regional Council had suggested'. The nub of the matter was that the Old Machar Park proposal was unusually complicated, since its boundaries included Gordon District as well as Aberdeen City. Eventually all concerned met for a discussion, the upshot of which was that Aberdeen City District went away to produce proposals for the park. When they returned with their report, a year later, they recommended that the Country Park idea be dropped in favour of 'tree planting and management schemes for the more sensitive areas such as Perwinnes Moss'. The afforestation plan was dying hard. In the meantime, they intended to further their plans to acquire Scotstown Moor and Corse Hill as a public open space. The Regional Planning Committee broadly agreed with the report's recommendations but, they went on, they preferred to 'review the matter in the context of Aberdeen Structure Plan'. All of this took a great deal of time and these events take us to 1977.

While the machinery of local government was lumbering away over the horizon, the suburbs of the city had crept up to the boundaries of Scotstown Moor. Rubbish dumping on the moor, long a minor problem, had now become quite serious, although few attempts were made to stop it. New housing was already extending along part of the moor's western marches and, in 1973, the builders moved in on the southern boundary. The developers, Salvesen Homes, made the most of Scotstown Moors attractions in their advertisements: 'Welcome to the great outdoors! ... Salvesen have taken one of the finest environments in the east of Scotland ... a magnificent setting!' Much of the magnificent setting was by now floundering under rusting tin cans and cast out refrigerators, but the wild flowers showed a surprising resilience. What looked like a rubbish dump in winter, became a blaze of colour in late May, the enjoyable sight of wildlife fighting back. No decision of any kind had yet been taken on the site's future however, although the amount of paperwork so far engendered would probably have been capable of carpeting the entire moor.

In 1977, Scotstown Moor changed hands again. This time the new owner wanted to develop it as a golf course, but wished to sell off six acres at the southern end for housing. After a protest was received from the Nature Conservancy Council, planning permission was refused. This might have been a good time for a new planning initiative, but the Regional planners were struggling with the labyrinthine complexities of the Aberdeen Area Structure Plan, and nothing worthwhile resulted, except for another batch of rather helpless meetings and discussions. The planners, perhaps impressed by the fuss being made over Scotstown Moor by 'conservationists', were warming to the idea of purchasing the site as a Local Nature Reserve. Their continued attempts to acquire the land, however, got nowhere.

The now ailing moor was dealt a near mortal blow in 1980. A proposed access road, linking a planned housing estate at North Denmore with the B.997, had been listed in the 23rd Amendment to the Aberdeen County Development Plan. Although several other routes were possible, this one was chosen and meant that it would be built across Scotstown Moor. The proposal had languished quietly for some years, when suddenly, in 1980, it became an alarming reality. What some had hoped would be a minor road turned out to be a metropolitan highway, with overhead lights and broad concrete pavements. It was also going to slice through the very heart of Scotstown Moor's wetlands. Fervent attempts were made to find a road alignment acceptable both to the contract surveyors and to a triumvirate of conservationists representing NCC, the University and the Scottish Wildlife Trust. For a while, a compromise solution appeared to have been reached. With this plan, the loss of wet heath was still serious, but the integrity of the moor would have been saved. Then, in early 1980, came the bombshell: the surveyors put in for permission for a completely different alignment, which would all but obliterate the best patch of bog on the entire moor. The reason, it transpired, was that someone had remembered that an underground water main crossed Scotstown Moor. If the compromise road alignment had been accepted, the water main would have required strengthening or diverting onto the road verges, and this would have cost someone a lot of money. The developers refused to pay. Aberdeen District Council refused to pay. Grampian Regional Council shrugged its corporate shoulders. The District Council, hitherto so dilatory in all its dealings with Scotstown Moor, speedily gave permission for the new road alignment against an impotent chorus of protest from conservation bodies, and, shortly afterwards, the bulldozers moved onto Scotstown Moor.

I visited the site in May 1981 to see what was left. The new road covers some of the moor's grassy flushes which were formerly dotted in June with the purple spikes of Marsh Orchids, and of a pool of open water which was the best refuge for most of the aquatic plants of the moor, less than a third remains. The long-term effect of the damming up by the road of the downhill flow of water remains to be seen, but its immediate effect has been to divide the moor, already a tiny, barely tenable fragment, into two more halves. Some of the rarer species such as Black Bog-rush have escaped the development, but the moor will soon be surrounded by new residential housing on three sides. To remain sanguine about its future now, requires deep reserves of optimism.

What went wrong? With hindsight, one might argue that Scotstown Moor was doomed from the moment it passed from the Bishopric to a private owner, or, alternatively, from the moment that the authorities scheduled its surroundings for high density residential development. The moor was an anachronism, preserved only by an antiquated system of land tenure. The flowers are interesting, but their main claim to 'uniqueness' is only in their proximity to the city. Is it worth all the fuss? I think that it is for three main reasons. Firstly, many people, and not just 'conservationists', still regard anachronisms as precious things. It would be a very dull world if we filled it entirely with things of the present and Scotstown Moor is, or was, as much part of Aberdeen's ancient heritage as Kings College or the Brig o' Balgownie. Unfortunately we have not yet learned to treat land with the same reverence that we treat our buildings and works of art. One could also argue that the many new schools in this area, present or planned, would have benefitted enormously from the preservation of a site as rich in wild interest as Scotstown Moor, provided that it was properly managed. One needs good sites close to home with the ever-increasing cost of transport. Finally there is the basic human need to have decent surroundings in which to live. All these principles seem to me to be worth fighting for. The sad thing is that one needs to fight at all.

As a rule, when town meets country, only sensitive and dynamic planning can save the scenery from disaster. Without it, the two are on a collision course; they become, in the words of the late Nan Fairbrother, 'a landscape of mutual destruction by two incompatible environments and the sickness infects them both'.[1] The local authority's greatest admirers could scarcely call their efforts over Scotstown Moor either sensitive or dynamic. I cannot blame the owners of the site for wishing to develop the land in the way their neighbours have done. But since all the Council Departments involved agree at least on the principle that the retention of the site is in the interests of the City, one might expect some vigorous attempt, for which they have adequate legal powers and financial resources, to save it. Instead, we have had ten years of endless futile meetings and interminable inter-departmental haggling in the place of decision and action.

But the question remains, what went wrong? Granted that the Councils *were* dilatory, *why* were they dilatory? Lack of finance, higher priorities, the intransigence of the landowners, District-Region difficulties, too-many-cooks-making-one-broth, all are possible candidates for an answer. I suspect a deeper underlying cause. I have a vivid memory of one particular meeting at Scotstown Moor, in November 1978. It was

1 New Lives New Landscapes (1970).

a bitterly cold day, but the District Council were there in force. A line of black limousines drew up along the track by the Scotstown Moor pool, an attractive enough place in the summer, but looking dismal and neglected in the grey light of winter. A rotting mattress lay half in, half out of the pool, and a litter of cans and plastic sacks strewed its nearside bank. I was asked if I would explain to the gentlemen what I found so interesting about this place. I had a go, attempting to raise my voice above their chattering teeth. As I spoke, the eyes of most of my audience glazed over with torpid disinterest. They glanced longingly at their cars and exchanged looks. Five minutes later, the shiny black saloons were roaring back to the warmth and tea-caddies of St Nicholas House and the moor lay deserted. I thought I knew then why Scotstown Moor was dying. The urban men of power were simply neither interested nor caring enough to save it.

FLOWERING PLANTS OF SCOTSTOWN MOOR

The following is a selection of the more interesting wild flowers of heath, grassland and bog recorded from Scotstown Moor between 1868 and 1980. The suggested causes of extinction of the lost plants of the moor is only tentative.

a) LOST PLANTS	b) SURVIVORS
?Lost through the reclamation of heath	Water Horsetail
	Wood Horsetail
	Marsh Marigold
Stagshorn Clubmoss	Lady-smock
Petty Whin	Heath Milkwort
Mountain Everlasting	Bog Violet
Bog Myrtle	Ragged Robin
Lesser Twayblade	Bitter Vetch
	Marsh Cinquefoil
?Lost through loss of open water	Grass of Parnassus
	Sundew
	Bog Willow-herb
Mares Tail	Marsh Pennywort
Bladderwort	Chickweed Wintergreen
Lesser Bladderwort	Bogbean
Shore-weed	Marsh Forget-me-not
Small Bur-reed	Red Rattle
	Lousewort
?Lost through improvement of grasslands	Butterwort
	Sea Plantain
	Marsh Arrow-grass
Least Clubmoss	Heath Spotted Orchid
Moonwort	Northern Marsh Orchid
Field Felwort	Lesser Butterfly Orchid
Frog Orchid	Fragrant Orchid
	Bog Asphodel

?Lost through the felling of pines	Bog Pondweed Cotton-grass Black Bog-rush
Twinflower Intermediate Wintergreen Creeping Lady's Tresses	Lesser Tussock Sedge Pale Sedge Tawny Sedge Flea Sedge
?Lost through diminution of marsh and bog	
Hairy Stonecrop Greater Sundew Fen Bedstraw Marsh Speedwell Many-stemmed Spike-rush Dioecious Sedge	
Lost for reasons unknown	
All-seed Chaff-weed Lesser Wintergreen Red Bartsia	

CORBY; LILY AND BISHOPS LOCHS: THE TRIPLE LOCHS

After the calamities of Tullos Hill and Scotstown Moor, it is pleasant to turn to an area which has remained comparatively unaffected by urban growth. Many British cities have retained islands of wilderness near to, or even within, the concrete jungle. Arthurs Seat in Edinburgh, Hampstead Heath in London's inner suburbs and Sutton Park in Birmingham are good examples. Perhaps Aberdeen's nearest and richest equivalent is an area of wet heath and open water which has come to be known as the Triple Lochs. These three small lochs owe their survival to their inaccessibility. Corby and Lily Lochs lie in a hollow surrounded by farmland, and no road, nor even a public footpath, leads to their shores. Even Bishops Loch, which lies immediately east of the busy B997, is an oddly elusive loch - one can easily whizz past it in a car without being aware of its existence. Nonetheless, the Triple Lochs all lie within an area of rapidly expanding suburban growth.

In a recent assessment of the natural history of Grampian region for planning purposes, Corby and Lily Lochs were the only site near to Aberdeen to score highly on no less than four different grounds: botanical, ornithological, entomological and ecological. Together with Bishops Loch, which forms an interesting contrast with the other two, they are incontestably the most important area of wetland near Aberdeen.

Indeed, one would need to venture as far as the Loch of Skene to find anything comparable. The Lochs of Park and Leys in lower Deeside were once of equal quality, but they have long since been drained. Corby and Lily Lochs closely resemble one another, which is not surprising since they lie in the same basin, and recent evidence from peat borings has shown that they were once parts of a single large body of water. The saucer-shaped basin is a kettle-hole, probably of the same type as those occupied by the lost lochs of Aberdeen City. Over the centuries the area and depth of the open water has gradually lessened as sediment and peat have begun to infill the basin, and reed-beds have encroached from the shores. This progression from open water to dry land is known as hydroseral succession, and a comparison of aerial photographs taken between 1948 and the present day shows that this process continues: three small pools between the two lochs have dried out completely, and scrub has formed on areas which were formerly wet heath. This suggests that the basin is drying out quite rapidly, in relative terms, and in the not too distant future the lochs may disappear altogether, particularly if attempts are made to improve the drainage. At present, though, we have a series of stages of succession from open water, through reedswamp and fen, to birch and sallow scrub. This is not only a diversity of habitat for wildlife, but is an excellent 'outdoor laboratory' for teaching and research into the dynamics of natural vegetation.

Of the two lochs, Corby is the best known. It is very shallow, and the deepest soundings taken were less than six feet although its water level fluctuates considerably with the seasons. Its waters are mesotrophic, or moderately base-rich, and this must owe something to the run-off of fertilisers from the surrounding agricultural land. Both White and Yellow Water-lilies grow wild in the sheltered bays of the loch, together with beds of the true Bulrush. The submerged vegetation is quite lush, consisting of at least five species of pond-weed, of which the commonest is the Grassy Pond-weed, together with Autumnal Starwort. The freshwater algae of Corby Loch were studied by Dickie in the last century, who discovered that its waters were coloured a dull green by two relatively uncommon species of blue-green algae in 1846 and 1848. On the northern and eastern shores of the loch, the fields pass directly down to the water, but the more sheltered shores have dense reed-beds and large stands of Bottle Sedge. A good variety of characteristic marsh plants are found about the margins, including Mares-tail, Marsh Cinquefoil, Marsh Arrow-grass, Bog Willow Herb, Marsh Woundwort, Marsh Pennycress and many others. Surrounding part of Corby Loch and the whole of Lily Loch, is wet heathland strewn with peat tussocks and dominated by heather and cotton-grass, with marshy 'poor-fen' in the places where peat has been cut. It has been suggested that this heath is of fairly recent origin, and has been encouraged by occasional fires. The birch and sallow scrub which, together with scattered pine and rowan, has colonised the drier parts of the heath, is certainly of recent origin, the bulk of it having grown up in the past thirty years.

Ninety two species of birds have been recorded from the Corby-Lily Loch basin, of which fifty six, including Little Grebe, Mallard, Teal, Tufted Duck and Merganser, have bred. The basin is also an important roost for farmland birds and the wildfowl of the lower Don valley. The lochs have small numbers of wintering Whooper Swans and are an irregular roost for Greylag Geese, with a recorded maximum of one thousand six hundred.

Bishop Loch differs from the other two in a number of ways. It lies in a separate basin and is not a kettle-hole, but a shallow, irregularly shaped pool, strikingly similar in shape to Parkhill Loch, a mile to the west. Bishops Loch was once a secluded tree-lined retreat of great beauty, and on its north shore are the remains of what is believed to be a Medieval manor and chapel, to which the bishops of Aberdeen would retire during times of trouble. The loch has not fared the passage of time as well as its companions to the east. Photographs of the loch taken in the early 1900s show a much broader expanse of water than exists there today, and there has clearly been a lowering of the water level. It is now so shallow that the eastern arm has silted up and is virtually choked by the lush growth of Bogbean, Water Horsetail, Bottle Sedge and Soft Rush. A nearby sand and gravel quarry is separated from the loch by an unsightly earthern bank, and new houses now run down to the loch shore from the north. Despite this, Bishops Loch is still one of the best freshwater bodies near Aberdeen. It is renowned locally for its spectacular spring migrations of toads. The invertebrate fauna forms an interesting contrast to that of Corby Loch. Bishops is more organically enriched, and contains species like the Horse Leech which do not occur in the other two. Bishops also has at least twenty species of water beetle, again many of them absent from Corby Loch. The fish, too, are different: pike and perch in Bishops, trout and eels in Corby. Finally Bishops Loch contains fewer species of freshwater molluscs than Corby, and no species at all of the hard water mayflies and stoneflies. The reason for this difference is still unclear, but it provides another dimension to the scientific interest of this trio of lochs.

The waters of Corby, Lily and Bishops Lochs were bought by Aberdeen County Council water services in 1955, as part of the then intended water supply for Dyce. On local Government reorganisation the lochs were on the boundary between Aberdeen and Gordon District and so, to simplify matters, they passed into the ownership of Grampian Regional Council Water Services Department. The land around the lochs, including the wet heath, remained in the private ownership of no less than six farms. Since the lochs were never linked up with Dyce's water mains, the Council was rather at a loss what to do with their property. Since any land (or water) in a Council's ownership has to be used for *something*, some sort of amenity role for the lochs seemed appropriate. The Triple Lochs therefore formed part of the still-born Old Machar Country Park scheme of the mid-seventies, which was also to encompass the remains of Scotstown Moor and an expanse of moorland called Red Moss. After the Country Park proposal fizzled out, the future of the lochs fell into abeyance for a year or two. Illegal fishing, and vandalism to neighbouring property, fencing and trees were taking place however, and at the end of 1978, the Director of Grampian Water Services came to a decision. The only means of preventing the illegal appropriation of Council property was to warden the site. This, he suggested, 'might best be done by establishing a Local Nature Reserve which, properly managed, would look after and control the recreational and scientific interests in the area'. The buck was thereupon passed to the regional Leisure and Recreation Department to implement the plan.

It was apparent that the Local Nature Reserve would need to include the privately-owned wetlands and heath surrounding the three lochs. The Leisure and Recreation committee decided against attempting to purchase this land, but they agreed to set up a working party representative of interested parties, and to approach the owners in the hope of obtaining their consent to a formal nature reserve agreement. Thereafter, progress was painfully slow. The proposed reserve offered no insuperable difficulties of management. It would require few resources and little or no active management; there was no easy access, and hence no problem with large numbers of visitors; there was no immediate 'threat' to the site. The 'interested parties' were broadly four: the scientists and naturalists, represented most prominently by the Scottish Wildlife Trust; local schools, particularly Powis Academy, who had built a boathouse on Corby Loch in the mid-seventies and often sailed its waters; Balgownie Angling Association who wanted formal permission to fish Corby Loch, and hoped to restock it; and occasional shooting parties after snipe and wild-duck. Of the six owners of the wetlands within the modest boundaries of the proposed reserve, four were reported to be agreeable to the idea in principle, and between them, they owned around eighty percent of the land. The signs, therefore, were propitious: meaningful discussions could begin, and there seemed to be no conflict of interest that common sense and goodwill could not overcome. But unfortunately, nothing much happened. The Leisure and Recreation Department showed no great enthusiasm for the project, and when two of six landowners refused to consider entering a nature reserve agreement, the officials appeared disheartened. When, at the beginning of 1981, the Scottish Wildlife Trust stepped in and offered to take over responsibility for setting up a reserve at the Triple Lochs, the Leisure and Recreation Department readily agreed. The SWT proposal was put up to the Council's Water Services committee in February. One Councillor present, is reported to have stated that 'any takeover by the Wildlife Trust could lead to a conflict of interests between the conservationists and the angling and sporting bodies'. Another disagreed and said that, on the contrary, 'the Wildlife Trust would satisfactorily safeguard and preserve the attractions of the area for the benefit of all those interested in its welfare'. And there, at the time of writing, the issue lies. The Scottish Wildlife Trust are currently awaiting the terms of a lease from the Water Services committee, which will enable them to set up, with the agreement of the landowners, a Trust reserve.

I, for one, believe that the Triple Lochs will eventually be a successful reserve and that potential conflicts of interest will be resolved. What I find so disappointing about the discussions so far on the future of this area, is the stagnation, once again, of the local authority concerned and their apparent lack of interest in nature conservation. Fortunately, the Councils' perennial ability to postpone decisions indefinitely, which proved fatal in the case of Scotstown Moor, has not unduly affected the quality of the Triple Lochs. But the opportunity to set up a Local Authority Nature Reserve near Aberdeen has slipped through their grasp. It seems strange to me that the City, which is so conscious and rightly proud of its prestige, should have let that opportunity slip so lightly.

Chapter 10

Aberdonian Naturalists

In this chapter we shall be looking at some of the men (for social reasons, possibly, there are no women) who, by their various labours of love, added to our knowledge of the natural history of Aberdeen. I have drawn a line at around 1920AD, partly because I feel that it is no business of mine to attempt to write about people still living, but also because there was a distinct change in the emphasis of local history at about that time. Hitherto, the neighbourhood of the city had furnished most of the localities which were regularly visited by natural history societies and university class excursions, and consequently the city's flora and fauna were documented in more detail than anywhere else. After 1920, the world changed: the old guard of Aberdonian naturalists were dead; most of the localities close to the city had been physically destroyed; and the increased availability of the internal combustion engine meant that excursion parties could now move further afield. Another factor, perhaps, was the shift in emphasis in biological science itself, away from the museum collections and detailed recording of the Victorian era, and towards more universal aspects of science. The result was a sudden diminution of published material on the natural history of Aberdeen.

The natural history tradition of Aberdeen blends the professionals and students of the University with amateurs from all walks of life, a healthy union which still continues. In Aberdeenshire, as in most other Scottish counties there has never been the large number of active amateur naturalists as there have long been in, say, Norfolk or Kent. Or, to be more accurate perhaps many of those who know Aberdeenshire's wildlife most intimately, belong to the separate pursuits of gamekeeping and forestry. Aberdeen University, on the other hand, has been one of the nation's leading centres of learning and research into the natural world for two centuries, and is one of the few British universities which still has a chair of Natural History. The present Masters course in ecology at Aberdeen, could be seen as a modern representation of this venerable tradition.

The seat of learning at Aberdeen was the product of one of the earliest glimmerings of the Scottish Renaissance. In 1494, a Papal Bull to Bishop Elphinstone sanctioned the establishment of a *studium generale* in Old Aberdeen, so that 'rude and barbarous' men might benefit from 'the pearl of Knowledge which shows the way to living well and happily'. The result of this was Kings College, which was followed a century later, to put the balance right, by Marischal College in New Aberdeen. Natural history was not on either college's curriculum until the end of the eighteenth century, but at least two Aberdonian graduates from the school of medicine made botanical reputations for themselves. James Cargill (c 1565-1616), a physician, was the first known Aberdonian to take an interest in local botany, for he used to send batches of wild flowers to a friend on the Continent, who published their names in a tome he named *Prodomus theatri botanici*. Among Cargill's specimens was the first record of that very characteristic north eastern flower, *Trientalis*, the Chickweed Wintergreen. Robert Morison (1620 - 1683) was the first Aberdonian botanist of national repute, but his career has little to do with his native city. As a committed royalist, he was forced to flee Aberdeen during the Civil War, and he took his Doctorate in exile in France. Perhaps because he had suffered for the Cause, he benefitted from royal patronage, and, after the Restoration, Charles II appointed him successively as court physician, Director of the Royal Garden at Kew and, finally, the first Professor of Botany at Oxford.

In 1788, Marischal College saw the light of the Age of Reason, and nominated James Beattie (d. 1810) to a new chair of Civil and Natural History. Beattie's syllabus was not confined to the living world and the main preoccupations of his school were physics, the weather, chemistry, anatomy, physiology plus, for good measure, a refresher course in Latin. Beattie himself took an interest in botany and contributed towards Sir James Smith's 'Flora of Britain'. Beattie is remembered as the discoverer of the north east's most famous wildflower, *Linnaea*, in 'a wood at Inglismadie, Mearnshire', in 1795.

The work of recording the flora of Aberdeen parish and county was already underway by about 1777, perhaps inspired by the Rev. John Lightfoot's *Flora Scotica*, which was first published in that year. George Don, the great Angus pioneer botanist, made periodic forays into the Cairngorms, returning with sack loads of botanical loot for his nursery garden in Forfar. Nearer to home, Dr David Skene was detailing the first records of lowland Aberdeen, which might have resulted in a published County Flora, had he not died in 1777, at the early age of thirty six. His manuscript notes still survive in the possession of Aberdeen University, and were incorporated into the later local floras.

By the early decades of the nineteenth century, amateurs and professionals were both engaged in the now fashionable sport of recording and collecting. Indeed, there were times when the desire to publish the definitive local flora seemed perilously close to a headlong race. In 1836, no less than three local floras reached the printers: George Dickie's *Flora Abredonensis*, Alexander Murray's *Northern Flora* (of which only the first quarter was completed before the author's death in 1837) and *Flora of Aberdeen* by Mr Cow, a local surgeon, whose work remained unpublished. Beattie's successors in the school of natural history of these years included Professor Knight, who made first discoveries of several British plants including *dickeiana*, the Dickie's Bladder-fern, and James Nichol, a geologist, who helped to solve one of Scotland's greatest natural mysteries, the parallel roads of Glen Roy.

Sad stories are told about two later nineteenth century naturalists. Robert Davidson was responsible for the museum collections of Aberdeen University, of which he had amassed many of the specimens himself. They were his pride and joy. Then, like many of his countrymen at that time, he left for the New World, took up a post in British Columbia, and, back at home, his collections fell into neglect. By the time he returned, many years later, most of his precious specimens, gathered and prepared with such pains, had been lost, filched or had simply fallen to pieces. John Duncan, a weaver of Alford, had even worse woes to endure. A keen botanist, he assembled a very fine herbarium of pressed plants, a lifetime's work, and left a legacy called the John Duncan Trust to science students at Alford School. In spite of this, his life was an unhappy one, according to the Third Statistical Account, 'full of hardship and misfortune, slighted by the eminent professors of Aberdeen, and hurt by the seeming indifference of his fellow men to the wonder and beauty of his collection of plants'. He was spared perhaps, the cruellest disappointment of all, for although he generously bequeathed his herbarium to the university, they promptly lost it. I am told that it may still be 'mouldering away somewhere in Marischal College'.

The nineteenth century was spanned by four men who together dominated those formative years of local natural history between 1820 and 1920, and they have been frequently mentioned and quoted in this book. Three of them, William MacGillivray, George Dickie and James Trail, were university professors who led distinguished academic careers. The fourth, George Sim, was a taxidermist and a leading amateur naturalist. All four spent much of their respective careers in the city of Aberdeen, and each had something new to say about its flora and fauna in their various publications. They had much in common in other ways. Their breadth of interest is perhaps the thing which most impresses one today; it embraced almost the whole natural world, but still left them free to specialise, MacGillivray in birds and geology, Dickie in algae, Trail in insects and rust fungi and Sim in fish and crustacea. Again, I feel that they must have shared rather similar dispositions; they were, to different degrees, solitary and independent men who nonetheless gave generously of their time and enthusiasm to those of like bent. They were Spartan in outlook, as serious field naturalists in the nineteenth century north east had to be, and indeed two of them eventually died from the effects of exposure. They all possessed acute powers of observation, the natural concomitant of a well-developed curiosity, and, fortunately for us, they shared a mania for recording, in minute detail, what they saw. Let us take a closer look at each of them.

WILLIAM MACGILLIVRAY [1796 - 1852]

William MacGillivray is probably Aberdeen's greatest field naturalist and certainly the one with the widest international reputation. He prepared the foundations for much of the later development of natural history at Aberdeen, and wrote a number of works which are still read today, but he is popularly remembered for his legendary capacity for physical endurance. MacGillivray was born in Old Aberdeen, but brought up on his uncle's farm on Harris - a wild solitude which may well have fashioned his subsequent outlook. From the age of twelve onwards, he attended Kings College, Aberdeen eventually taking the degree of A.M. and going on to study medicine. At the end of each session, he usually returned to the west coast on foot. Such journeys must have demanded a capacity for self-denial and acceptance of extreme discomfort, hunger and cold almost unimaginable today, but the young MacGillivray was only one among many students who likewise braved the wilderness. His epic journey to the British Museum in London however, places him in a bracket on his own. Wishing to see for himself, the 'great collections of Beasts and Fishes, of Birds & other flying things, of Reptiles & Insects - in short of all the creatures which have been found upon the face of the earth', he duly set out, on foot, at first light on September 7th, 1819. Not content with taking the most direct route to London, he made a diversion through the Highlands to Fort William, subsisting largely on barley bread and spring water. When he crossed the border, his few Scottish banknotes were refused, and by the time he reached London, in the pouring rain, on October 20th, having covered over eight hundred miles, he was unspeakably weary and his clothing was in rags. Nothing daunted, he inspected the British Museum the next day, and returned to Aberdeen a week later, by steamboat.

In 1820, he married and moved to Edinburgh University as assistant to Professor Robert Jameson in the Department of Natural History. One of Jameson's novel ideas had been to introduce field classes in geology to Britain, and he often made a practice of lecturing on site, in the open air. This was something new: direct contact with nature rather than with dried cabinet specimens struck a responsive chord with MacGillivray and he introduced similar procedures at Marischal College, Aberdeen, when he was appointed Professor of Civil and Natural History there in 1841. By this time, he had already written one well known book, *Description of the Rapacious Birds of Great Britain* (1836), and completed the first three volumes of his *magnum opus*, *A History of British Birds*, illustrated with his own fine engravings of avian viscera - he subsequently referred, with deprecative modesty, to the whole vast compilation as 'all guts and gizzards'.

The curriculum inherited by MacGillivray at Aberdeen covered moral and natural philosophy, mathematics, chemistry, Latin and Greek as well as natural history in the modern sense of the word. Among this pot-pourri of abstract thought, the study of living plants and animals had been almost lost sight of. MacGillivray brought a new emphasis to bear on zoology, comparative anatomy and geology, as well as a strong leavening of local natural history. His search for the truth always led him to the source: the living world. Although he transformed and enriched the College museum, he scorned the vast majority of his contemporaries, who neglected living things in favour of cabinet specimens and skins. To those, like the young Darwin, who shared his independent outlook, MacGillivray could be kind and generous; those who didn't probably found him rather tiresome.

MacGillivray's *History of Molluscous Animals of the Counties of Aberdeen, Kincardine and Banff* (1843) was a milestone in local zoology, as was his paper on the Daubenton's bats of St Machar Cathedral, which placed Aberdeen city on the naturalist's map. In other respects, he was unlucky in his publications. His *British Birds* was overshadowed by William Yarrell's work of the same title, which was more speedily completed and proved the more popular. The last two volumes of *British Birds* were not published until the year of MacGillivray's death, and were completed 'in sorrow and sickness'. Nor was there a second edition.

A Natural History of Deeside and Braemar, which V. C. Wynne-Edwards has called 'his most perfect and harmonious work' was not printed until three years after his death, and even then only by the royal prompting of Victoria and Albert. In this sublime book, MacGillivray's wide interests and intimate knowledge merge with a gift for lyrical description and feeling for the natural world, which has never lost its power to move the reader. In it he sets out his own philosophy more clearly than in his other works:

'... a single-minded man may by a right use of his eyes, anywhere that the sun shines, and the winds blow, and the rains fall, find abundant matter for observation and instruction,'

and, by way of a corollary,

'He who finds no pleasure in simply gazing on the fair face of nature, has a soul deadened to all that is capable of conferring true happiness.'

Deeside and Braemar is among the last published works in which all nature was seen as a manifestation of God's creation, rather than what it has subsequently come to be - an open-air laboratory, subject to natural laws. Perhaps as a result, MacGillivray could put into words the feeling of *being* on the hill and the joy of making new discoveries and a century later, it still reads with remarkable freshness. His religious convictions did not mean that his outlook was conservative. His *'Remarks on the Phanerogamic Vegetation of the River Dee'* (1832), in which he examines the vegetation at different stages along the river valley, has been called 'the earliest of all British ecological studies.' [1]

When MacGillivray died (suitably enough from the effects of exposure) in 1852, he bequeathed a tradition of field natural history based on the observation of living things, which continues to characterise Aberdeen University. As a man, MacGillivray eludes us. We know what he did, and what some of his ideas were, but it is difficult to imagine a conversation with him. We do not even know what he looked like, for he evidently refused ever to sit for a portrait. But his voice speaks out clearly from the pages of *A Natural History of Deeside and Braemar* and he is a very agreeable companion.

Footnote
A Natural History of Deeside and Braemar is a fairly rare book in the original, and commands a corresponding price tag. Perhaps someone could be persuaded to reprint it?

GEORGE DICKIE [1813 - 1882]

George Dickie, the author of the only flora to date of the north eastern counties, lived for most of his life in the same Aberdeen house in which

1   John Raven, in Chapter 1 of Mountain Flowers, Collins (1956).

he was born. His interest in natural history was inbred at an early age, and by the time he took his MA at Marischal College in 1830, he was already well acquainted with the flora and fauna of his native county. He went on to study medicine at Aberdeen and Edinburgh, with botany as a sideline, and was lecturer in botany at Kings College between 1839 and 1849, and a contemporary and friend of MacGillivray. On his departure, he was awarded an honorary MD by the College in recognition of his services. During this period he produced his first local flora, *Flora Abredonensis* (1836), today a rather little-known work which Dickie later expanded into his better known *Botanist's Guide* of 1860. He was also a founding member of the first known natural history society in Aberdeen, in around 1845.

Between 1849 and 1860, Dickie was Professor of Natural History at the University of Belfast, which resulted in his second flora, the *Flora of Ulster* (1864). In 1860, he returned from what must have seemed like an exile to his native city, where he was appointed to the new chair of botany, following the union of Marischal and Kings Colleges to form the University of Aberdeen. Almost at once, tragedy struck. Shortly after his return, Dickie spent several days botanising in the hills around Braemar. The weather was at its appalling worst, and Dickie went down with exposure, which later aggravated into bronchitis and deafness, afflictions which persisted to the end of his life. This disaster coincided with the publication of Dickie's best-remembered work, the *Botanist's Guide to the Counties of Aberdeen, Banff and Kincardine*. This was an unusually ambitious flora, for not only did it encompass an area half the size of Wales, but also covered the entire plant kingdom from flowering plants and ferns to mosses, fungi and algae. Dickie was at pains to add supplementary information which we would now call ecological, such as the altitudinal ranges of each plant. It is a measure of Dickie's achievement that the *Botanist's Guide* remains to this day a useful handbook and it has never been superseded.

The forty or so pages of the *Botanist's Guide* which Dickie devoted to algae reflect his life-long interest in this neglected group, of which he was probably the greatest expert of his time. He identified quantities of these difficult organisms from various global expeditions, but he never underwent extensive travel himself. Perhaps his uncertain health prevented him. Several newly discovered algae were named in his honour, including a genus of diatoms called *Dickieia*, but most British botanists will be more familiar with the rare Aberdonian fern, *Cystopteris dickeiana*, named after Dickie by Professor Knight in the 1840s. One of Dickie's last acts, before continued ill health forced his retirement, was to found the Scottish Cryptogamic Society, which was

Fig. 15. George Dickie, Professor of Botany, 1860-1877.

Fig. 16. J. W. H. Trail, Professor of Botany, 1877-1919.

established in order to encourage interest in the groups of primitive plants, which were his chiefest interest.

Dickie retired in 1877, and the empty Chair of Botany was filled his former pupil, James Trail. A year before he died, he was honoured by membership of the Royal Society. Trail's obituary of Dickie describes him as a 'most kind and obliging friend, on whose kindness and goodwill full reliance could at all times be placed.'

JAMES WILLIAM HELENUS TRAIL [1851 -1919]

It has been said of the academic Aberdonian that his natural bent is 'for minute, detailed work; for accuracy in the small things'. If anyone could be said to epitomise that tradition, in the best sense of the phrase, it was James William Helenus Trail. Trail was to chronicle the plant life of Aberdeen City in minute and (to some people at least) fascinating detail, and contribute scores of minor papers on Scottish natural history, but never produced a work of national influence. Like MacGillivray, Trail spent his boyhood on what was then a remote island. He was born in Orkney in 1851, the youngest child of the Parish Minister of Birsay, and was said to be so small and puny at birth 'that it was found impossible to dress him, and he was rolled in cotton wool and fastened to the pillow; his face was just the size of his father's watch face.' Trail was fascinated by natural history almost from the moment he first drew breath, and the headlands and moors of Birsay provided wildlife in plenty. In 1862, he was sent to school in Aberdeen and went on to take an honours degree in natural science. By 1870, Trail virtually ran the zoology museum, which he regarded as a labour of love, and was taking a leading hand in Professor Dickie's botany excursions.

In 1873, Trail interrupted his studies in medicine for the opportunity to take part in an exploration of the Amazon, for which he had been recommended by Dickie. This eighteen month journey, in which Trail fulfilled a dual role as botanist and medical officer, must have had the same invigorating influence on him that the voyage of the Beagle had on Charles Darwin, forty years before. Trail had a natural aptitude for describing and cataloguing living things never seen before. Eventually eighteen species and two genera of newly discovered Amazonian wildlife were named after him: a mixed bag of algae, bugs, butterflies, lichens, palms, fungi and beetles. Shortly after his return, Trail obtained his medical degree with flying colours, and went on to inherit the Chair of Botany at the age of only twenty six, after the retirement of George Dickie. He held this post for over forty years, to the end of his life.

1   Professor James Ritchie, Aberdeen University Review, XV.

Trail was never a fluent lecturer and, characteristically, he attempted to overcome his shyness by learning his lectures off by heart. His influence, however, both within the Science Faculty and on Scottish natural history generally, was considerable. He was editor of the Scottish Naturalist (1892-1890), edited the Annals of Scottish Natural History (1892-1911), and presided over the new upsurge of local interest embodied in the Aberdeen Working Men's Natural History and Scientific Society (q. v.). To these journals he contributed a stream of papers, especially on his own pet interests of butterflies and moths, galls, spiders, snails and rust fungi. The latter specialisation resulted in the discovery of several more new species.

The local flora of Aberdeen City, in which he spent most of his life, always fascinated Trail. One of the saddest aspects of his life must have been to witness the destruction of every one of the places in which he and Dickie used to lead regular botanical excursions. He chronicled the transformation of a small city in close contact with relatively wild places, to a modern metropolis of lawn grass and concrete, and although he was not given to passionate denunciation, his sense of anger sometimes breaks through the calm prose of his *Flora of Aberdeen.*

Trail's Obituarist remarks that his life was 'regulated by a Spartan simplicity, a devotion to duty, a fearless uprightness and a sturdy belief in the justice of his cause'. He certainly demanded enthusiasm from his students, one of whom recalled those gruelling, foodless country rambles which lasted from eight in the morning until late in the afternoon. Those who were driven by similar fires usually found the experience worthwhile. Trail was always a meticulous recorder of his observations, and his listed publications take up eighteen pages of the Memorial Volume which incorporates his flora. It was this painstaking eye for detailed research that led him into taking a keen amateur interest in genealogy. Very characteristically, Trail managed, by meticulous research, to trace his own familial descent back through ten centuries, to his ancient forbear, King Duncan.

At the end of his life, Trail was a pillar of the scientific establishment, and he died in harness. By that time, he had been nominated Dean of the Science Faculty, Fellow of the Royal Society and was one of the last Provosts of Old Aberdeen. The students of his department unveiled a tablet to his memory, for 'inspiring successive generations of students with his desire for deeper knowledge'. The tablet presents a rather stern, General Kitchener-like profile of Trail, which is strangely at variance with his portrait photographs. These show an earnest-looking man with unusually large eyes and ears, perhaps fitting attributes for a great observer of nature, together with a determined chin which he sometimes covered with a beard. The stiff, respectable pose which he always struck before a camera, is lightened by his expression which was invariably honest, shy and kindly. He looked the part of a man whose maxim throughout life was the one which has characterised most of Britain's great naturalists: 'Observe and observe again, for observation is the foundation of Truth'.

GEORGE SIM [1835 - 1908]

MacGillivray, Dickie and Trail were professional scientists. George Sim, on the other hand, was a leading representative of the other wing of the movement, the amateur naturalist. Born in Craigellachie on Speyside, Sim's upbringing was typical of the terrible hardship in country areas of that time. His father did his best to provide for his large family by a variety of livelihoods, but at Turiff, where for a while he was a farm grieve, he lost no less than five of his family inside two years; others were invalids. Sim, not surprisingly, had little formal education. He was made apprentice to a tailor at the age of thirteen, and began to make a premature independent living as a journeyman tailor, after his master became an alcoholic. Sim probably found this existence purgatory. In 1857, he settled at Aberdeen, where, with one of his surviving brothers, he opened a druggists shop.

What spare time life had so far afforded him, Sim often devoted to rambling in the country, sometimes taking a spirit stove with him and staying out all night. One of his main interests lay in marine life, and Aberdeen offered the opportunity to visit the fish market early in the morning, where unusual fish and crustacea were often brought in on the trawlers. Sim's other chief interest was in taxidermy, and the demand for his skill in this art led him, in 1862, to try the experiment of opening his own taxidermist's shop in King Street. He was delighted and, probably, surprised by the success of this venture, which gave him, at last, a congenial livelihood in which he could devote more time to his interests.

From 1862 until 1890, Sim kept a meticulous record of his observations of local natural history, which eventually extended over twelve quarto books. This journal, which still survives, is crammed with information, some of which was eventually used as a basis for his *magnum opus, The Vertebrate Fauna of Dee* (1903). Sim worked on the material of this book for twelve years, devoting so much of his time to it that he was forced to abandon his journal. The *Vertebrate Fauna* does for Deeside vertebrates what Dickie's and Trail's floras did for the plant world, although Sim's chosen title is a little misleading since his 'Dee' also includes the marine fishes and whales of the North Sea! Sim recorded a time when the persecution of carnivores and raptors had reached its height, and his pages document their steady decline on Deeside, in some cases to extinction.

Sim was said to be an 'omnivorous' reader, perhaps because he was self-conscious about his lack of formal education. He was physically of spare frame and ascetic appearance, which belied his capacity for long hill walks and his comparatively long life. He was said to be often reserved and silent, apparently dour, in company - he was probably easily bored by claptrap, a common failing among naturalists. His oracular knowledge of local natural history was eventually aknowledged by the scientific establishment in 1886, when the Linnean Society awarded him an Associate Membership, no mean distinction for an amateur in those days.

LOCAL NATURAL HISTORY SOCIETIES

The natural history field club was one of the more enduring inventions of the early part of Queen's Victoria's reign. New ideas are often slow to take root in Aberdeen, and although there were two successive local natural history societies between 1845 and 1863, little is known about them, and they evidently did not publish anything. The third, the Natural History Society of Aberdeen, was more long-lasting. It held its inaugural meeting in November 1863, and subsequently met regularly in the winter months, during which papers would be read on a wide variety of topics. Only two early publications survive: a paper written by John Sim on 'the Botany of Scotston Moor', and a Transactions of 1878, which includes a review by the newly appointed Professor Trail , on 'the Progress of Zoology in Aberdeen and its Neighbourhood'. Indeed, Trail appears to have been the life and soul of the society at that stage, for the bulk of the Transactions is taken up with his own voluminous lists of Lepidoptera, aphids, galls and spiders. The Society, later transformed into the Aberdeen Natural History and Antiquarian Society, published four substantial books which are still widely used for reference. The first three were concerned with inanimate objects: the Physical Geology of the Dee (1912) and the Don (1921), both by Alexander Bremner, and the Old Deeside Road (1921) by Aberdeen's City Librarian, G. M. Fraser. The latter has been reprinted recently in a limited paperback edition, and quickly sold out. The fourth publication was to be Trail's long awaited *Flora of the City Parish of Aberdeen*, but Trail died before it could be published. The Committee of the Society decided to honour his memory with a special volume, incorporating a 'biographic sketch' and a complete bibliography, in addition to the Flora. The Trail Memorial Volume was finally published by Aberdeen University Press in 1923, and it forms one of the most detailed records of a city's plant life that has ever been written. With this culminating effort, the Society seems to have exhausted itself, although it languished on until 1963.

In the meantime, a more lively 'grass-roots' society had been set up in 1886, which relied less on University patronage. It was given the cumbersome title of the Aberdeen Working Men's Natural History and Scientific Society, with William Cowie, an amateur Ledidopterist, as its first president. The small 'band of working men' who founded the club were fired with proselytising zeal. Their aim was not only to study local natural history, but 'to spread a knowledge of, and foster a love for, natural history among those outside its membership'. The Society gave its first public exhibition of specimens in 1889, in their small meeting rooms at Nelson Street. Whatever was in that display, it attracted public curiosity and interest, and the burgeoning Society was soon on the look-out for more spacious quarters. In 1899, they obtained permission from the University senate to meet at Marischal College, and Trail gave a helping hand by putting the botanical classroom at their disposal.

Two years later, the Society published their first Transactions, printed at the Daily Journal office for the price of ninepence each. The avowed aim of the Transactions was to provide 'good local lists', thus replacing one of the functions of the older Natural History Society. Lectures and discussions were also frequent items, and the pages of the Transactions provide ample evidence of the enthusiasm and avidity for knowledge which characterised such meetings. On September 17th, 1901, for instance, discussion included the following pressing matters:

> Is electricity and life one and the same thing?
> How is it that a dragon fly can fly backwards?
> Do puffins cast their bills in winter?

Two months later, a Mr Grigor put a more controversial argument to his fellow members: 'Man, is he the Product of Evolution or Creation?' Mr Grigor favoured the latter alternative.

The exhibitions were also a great success. In the month following the discussions on electricity and puffin's bills, an exhibition of brass microscopes and slide specimens attracted over four hundred visitors in the space of two hours. These exhibitions were often like miniature museums, full of the curiosities and conversation pieces which so delighted the Victorians. A typical exhibition included the following cosmopolitan selection:

from Mr A Benzie: Tortoise and eggs, parasites from same, Maori
                         paddles and sword.

Mr A Brown: 3 carved black marbles (Nineveh), silver ore
                         (Siberia), 2 fine specimens of giant lizard's
                         teeth (Kentucky), 2 marine fossils (Rothesay),
                         native amber (Aberdeen beach).

Mr J Davidson: Microscopical specimens, mathematical
                         puzzles.

Mr Geo. Reay: Moth, scorpion, beetles, nest of trap-door
                         spider from Bloemfontein; large cairngorm.

Mr Jas. Smith: Elephant's Teeth.

Mr Geo. Spark: Tarantulas, scorpions, Egyptian corn (Egypt).

Mr H D Welsh: 2 adders from Sgor Mor, Glen Dee; large
                         photograph of Loch Avon and Cairngorm.

In quite another sense, the Society showed an open-ness of mind
well in advance of the time: ladies were admitted as full members from
1903 onwards.

The summer months were given over to field excursions which show
an impressive breadth of interest, matching that of the exhibitions.
Places visited in 1903 included Aberdeen Ice Works, the Corporation
Electricity Works, GNS Railway Locomotive Works at Inverurie, Dun-
nottar Castle and the grounds and hothouses of Thomas Ogilvy at
Kepplestone. The Transactions also make all too brief references to
natural history excursions to nearby localities, with Scotstown Moor
leading the field, and the secluded vales of Corbie Den, Rubislaw Den
and the Den of Maidencraig not far behind.

The Working Men's Society (from 1903 onwards, perhaps it should
technically have been called the Working Persons' Society) published
their Transactions annually at first, but the time interval between each
issue gradually became more irregular, and, like many another club in
Aberdeen and elsewhere, it was killed off by the Great War. A partial
replacement, although not a conscious successor, was the Deeside Field
Club, founded in 1920, which has followed a similar programme of
winter lectures and summer visits to this day. Its magazine, the Deeside
Field, has published many articles of quality, with an emphasis on local
and natural history.

The clubs and societies which are actively involved at present in the
study and conservation of Aberdeen's wildlife are the Scottish Wildlife
Trust, the Northern Naturalist's Union and, from a slightly different
standpoint, the local branches of the Conservation Society, Friends of
the Earth and the Conservation Corps. There are also various depart-
mental university societies. The Aberdeen University Bird Club is

particularly active, and numbers beached bird surveys, wildfowl and wader counts and common bird census work among its regular activities. They publish an annual report giving details of birds records throughout the north east and, since 1975, the data has been stored on the ICL computer at Aberdeen Computing Centre. An energetic local bird ringing group has also been established, which represents a continuing local tradition dating back to the early 1900s, when Landsborough Thomson set up a ringing system based at the university.

The Aberdeen branch of the Scottish Wildlife Trust has maintained a steady growth in its membership in recent years - no mean feat in times of rampant inflation - and its combination of summer outings and winter talks and films draw in good numbers. Inevitably, the conservation of local wildlife is in the forefront of its concern, and the modern emphasis on conservation is the chief difference between it and the natural history societies of the days when the pace of life was more leisurely. But the chief motivation of its members - the love of nature - has not changed over the decades.

Chapter 11

Man's Dominion

'The social friendly, honest man,
Whate'er he be,
'Tis he fulfils great Nature's plan,
And none but he!'

Robert Burns
Second Epistle to Laphraik

In the preceding chapters of this book I have tried to indicate something of the variety of wildlife harboured within the boundaries of Aberdeen City District. It was a much larger task than I knew when I first began this book and although I have attempted to cover the main themes, there is a great deal more that must be left unsaid. Perhaps this is as it should be: an understanding of natural history is best gained by using ones ears and eyes, and books should not pretend to be anything more than a guide.

Most urban and suburban wildlife can be divided into two kinds. There are those which have adapted to the urban environment and thrive in it, such as the roof-nesting Oystercatchers and gulls or the wild flowers of Rubislaw Terrace. The townscape is never static, indeed it is currently developing at a disconcerting pace, but however artificial our surroundings become, they will assuredly never be sterile of life. Then there is the other kind of wildlife - the great majority - whose natural haunts have been reduced to small islands amid an urban and agricultural ocean. For these, life is a struggle for survival, a struggle which many have already lost. The pressures on Aberdeen's remaining wild islands are such that without some form of protection, they may not survive for very much longer.

But of course this begs the question: do we really want a variety of wildlife in and near to the city? The implication of some of the public reports and plans produced by Aberdeen's local government is that most people either don't or don't care, and that planning for wildlife is little

*Estimated areas of semi-natural vegetation
within Aberdeen City District*
(figures based on an internal NCC report by Peter Thomas)

	Area in hectares	Percentage of the total area of the District
Broad-leaved woodland:		
beech	52	0.3)
birch	81	0.4) 1.1
mixed	90	0.5)
alder	0.5	
Mixed woodland:	16	0.1
Wetland:	103	0.6
Heathland:		
wet heath	65	0.4) 2.57
dry heath	386	2.17)
Total	793.5	4.37
Total area of build-up land	5730	31.06
Total area of District	18447	

more than a bone to throw at those small fringe groups who are usually clumped together as 'the conservationists'. This is a demonstrably short-sighted view. Nature has influenced many of mankind's greatest artistic achievements and has given simple pleasure and joy to countless millions, long before the word conservationist was first employed. In a natural history of the West Midlands conurbation called 'The Endless Village', W G Teagle suggested that 'conservation measures ...will affect more than plant and animal life; they will, if the mind of man is influenced at all by his surroundings, have their effect on human society as well'. If one accepts that logical premise, then the need for wildlife in our cities, where most of us now live, is not one confined to any specialist group; it concerns us all. I believe the nature conservation argument applied to city areas is often presented back to front. There is seldom any urgent need to find a place for nature on disinterested or preservationist grounds: if Aberdeen was coated from top to bottom with concrete and then sprayed with poisonous chemicals, it would probably not make a significant difference to the wildlife resources of the north eastern counties, let alone Scotland or Britain. It is we who, consciously or unconsciously, have a need for nature, and by looking after nature we are looking after ourselves. It is this universal aspect which is consistently ignored by both local and national government legislation.

Highly elaborate conservation schemes do of course exist, and Aberdeen's local authorities have two forms of site safeguard within its planning procedures. Let us take a necessarily brief look at how nature conservation in Aberdeen actually operates. The main burden falls on the District and Regional authorities, who, in turn, rely on advice from three main representative bodies: the local societies, particularly the Scottish Wildlife Trust, who, in effect, represent local people with an interest in natural history; the university, who give impartial scientific advice via a committee called the Environmental Liaison Group, and who are also sometimes concerned as individuals with local conservation issues; and the Nature Conservancy Council, the Government agency responsible for nature conservation in Britain, who have a regional office in Aberdeen. The NCC, the SWT and the local authorities have all established a network of nature reserves in Scotland but, as yet, there are no reserves within Aberdeen District's boundaries. There is no land, therefore, which is managed *primarily* for the objective of nature conservation. There are, however, two systems which seek to provide protection to small areas which are designated as of special interest. The 'official' NCC system is that of the Site of Special Scientific Interest, which is usually abbreviated as SSSI. SSSIs are notified to the local authority who are thereupon obliged to invite NCC's comments on any planning application within the boundaries of an SSSI. It is, at best, an imperfect system of safeguard, since the decision whether or not to give planning permission rests entirely with the local authority (there are exceptions to this generalisation but they do not apply to Aberdeen city). The interests of such sites can also be destroyed, quite legally, without planning permission being necessary, for example by agricultural operations.

There are only six SSSIs within Aberdeen District, and these are as follows:

SSSI	*Principal conservation interest*
Scotstown Moor	Wet heath and bog.
Corby and Lily Loch	Open water, reedbed and bog
Loirston Loch	Open water and margins
Cove Coast	Flora of coastal cliffs
Balgownie Bridge	Geological exposure
Nigg Bay	Geological exposure

In addition, the river Dee as far downstream as Cults Island, is a

Grade One site, of national importance as the best example of a oligo-trophic or base-poor river system in Britain. The SSSIs are not neces-sarily the richest sites within Aberdeen District, nor are they neces-arily the ones which interest local naturalists most, but they do represent the most 'important' in a wider north eastern context. They are all very small and together they total only a fraction of a percent of the land surface of Aberdeen District. They are also essentially rural sites, and for those which now lie close to built-up areas, such as Scotstown Moor or Nigg Bay, SSSI protection has not been strong enough to safeguard them against urban pressures on the land.

This leaves us with the second protective system, which was devised jointly in 1977 by Aberdeen University and Grampian Regional Council. The scheme is a complex one, involving sites of three grades of relative importance and a variety of different subject headings such as botany, ornithology, freshwater, geology and archeology. An academic 'referee' was nominated for each subject, who was responsible for drawing up a list of what informed scientific opinion regarded as the most important sites within Grampian region. These included the existing SSSIs. These sites were first termed 'Environmentally Sensitive Areas' or SESAs, but this was later changed to the slightly better 'Sites of Interest to Natural Science' or SINS. The Regional Council recommended that the scheme should be adopted by the Districts, including Aberdeen City, and it has since become part of normal planning practice. Needless to say, SINS designation provides no better protection to the sites than SSSI, but the scheme nonetheless has two not inconsiderable merits. Firstly it enables local scientists and naturalists to give an opinion on planning applications affecting SINS. Secondly it gives a form of protec-tion to a much greater number of sites than the SSSI system on its own can provide, including sites which are not significant nationally but are of great value to local naturalists.

Any scheme based on site selection, however, has grave inherent defects, for which it is not easy to provide a solution. Such a system is founded on the premise that nature can be packaged into finite chunks of land, like a crop of carrots, and however neat this idea might seem on a drawing board, it bears little resemblence to reality - nature is every-where and we are part of it. It leads on to the notion that a certain small number of sites are 'important' and the rest of the land is unimportant. I find a more practical defect far more grave however. The best-laid plans are only successful if they work in practice. It is perhaps too early to judge the SINS scheme, but in nearly all recent test cases, develop-ment has prospered at the expense of nature. In the end, most issues boil down to the basic one of cost: the road through Scotstown Moor, for instance, could have been made less damaging, but only at the expense of strengthening the water main; the perennial rubbish dumping problem could be solved, but only by methods which would raise the rates. Since the benefits of nature conservation are not quantifiable in terms of cost, they fare poorly in most planning decisions which are usually based on pecuniary and short-term grounds. The social benefits of nature conservation to the community as a whole are consistently under-rated. In Aberdeen's case there may be historical reasons for this: Aberdeen's very presence is, to a great extent, man's triumph over the hostile wilderness, and the spirit of improvement is still a powerful social force in which nature can all too easily be regarded as the enemy. So far then, the site selection schemes have signally failed to protect even the very limited areas of ground which they cover. The question we are therefore entitled to ask is: are the planning procedures for nature conservation anything more than mere window-dressing? In a wider sense, when faced with a choice between short-term gain and longer-term nature conservation, are there any conceivable circumstances in which the former course would not be chosen?

There is an interesting contrast at Aberdeen between the lack of public money invested in protecting the few remaining wild places, and the vast expense poured into maintaining short grass and flower beds in almost every open space within the city. This is understandable in the urban parks, where such expense can perhaps be justified in terms of popular demand. In places like Donmouth and Girdleness, it is far less excusable and far more damaging to wildlife. Here we are faced with the ludicrous spectacle of the city's main amenity body spending a great deal of money getting rid of one of the city's big amenities: its bird life. There is a frightening contrast between the efficiency of the parks managers on the one hand, and the evident lethargy and lack of political will of those responsible for putting site protection schemes into practice on the other. The former are busy wiping out many of the city's remaining corners of wild ground by their mania for tidiness, and the latter have not done a great deal in practice to save the remaining rural sites from the consequences of urban growth.

But of course, it is facile to blame everything on local government. Most of the authorities' actions have a social cause, and the high maintenance philosophy of the parks managers is, I feel, there partly to combat the menace of vandalism and rubbish dumping. A patch of wild ground near a city represents, in some people's eyes at least, an open invitation to dump rubbish, dig turf or shoot at anything that moves, whereas short grassland and flowers 'that bloom as they are told' are a public extension of private gardens and therefore sacrosanct.

One curiosity of Aberdeen is that although, so far as my own observations go, people do not pick wild flowers to any significant extent, they are avid bird nesters and some even catch live song birds. Birds such as Mute Swans or terns have an uphill struggle to raise a brood anywhere near the city except on the inaccessible or carefully guarded sites.

There is much that individuals can do in the field of urban nature conservation if they wish. I would suggest three possible areas of activity. Firstly, if there is an attractive area of rough ground within your neighbourhood, propose that the local residents association or school 'adopt' it as a 'back-garden nature reserve'. This has already happened in the case of Arnhall Moss at Westhills. This need not imply any restriction on human access, and a caring approach to the problem of a small fragile site can produce an asset which benefits - and does credit to - the whole community. Secondly, you can register your vote for nature conservation by joining, if you have not already done so, the Aberdeen branch of the Scottish Wildlife Trust. The more members the Trust has, the more notice local government tend to take of their advice, and there are numberless opportunities to take a more lively role in the Trust's various activities. Thirdly, if you see an area you know and love deteriorating into an eyesore, don't sit back and do nothing: lobby your local Councillor, contact the Environmental Health Department, write to anyone you can think of, including the landowner and the local press. Make an issue of it; many of the atrocities which have happened to Aberdeen are not the inevitable results of progress, they are the opposite - the results of mindlessness and barbarism.

There is also a great deal that local authorities could do, without raising the rates. In the town's open spaces, a relatively small reduction in the present high intensity of maintenance would benefit wildlife enormously. Mowing regimes could be relaxed in some areas, and the grass left uncut until the end of June. Commercial 'conservation' seed mixtures containing various colourful wild flowers could be sown, instead of monocultures of grass. More native trees could be planted and dead wood left lying in wooded corners. Streams could be left unculverted with wild, uncut banks. Above all, we could do with some good ponds, instead of the present concrete tanks and paddling pools which are almost as sterile of life as a bath-tub. The parks authorities must know about such possibilities. Unfortunately, either through inbred conservatism and long tradition, or because they regard such measures in rather the same way as a cereal farmer regards a crop of weeds, the parks managers have often failed to contemplate them. A more fundamental step of lasting benefit, which could be taken by either of (or both) the District and Regional planning authorities, would be to employ a professional ecologist on their staff. It would be easy for them to reject this suggestion in the present economic blight (although some Scottish regional authorities do have an ecologist on their staff), but among the hordes that beaver away from nine till five in St Nicholas and Woodhill Houses, one could, I imagine, find people whose everyday tasks are of rather less import. Reliance on the advice of external bodies, such as NCC, is not an adequate substitute for a man on the spot who could inject some much-needed environmental expertise into a broad range of Council policies.

Local authorities claim that they are the executors of public will, and are sensitive to public opinion. It is perhaps with the public that hope ultimately resides, and there is at present an international attempt to generate public interest and debate in urban wildlife conservation, launched by the Council of Europe in October 1980, with the imposing title of 'the Campaign for Urban Renaissance'. The Manpower Services Commission, the British Trust for Conservation Volunteers and ad hoc action groups like Friends of the Earth, have all contributed to local projects, which are set out to generate enthusiasm and a sense of involvement from the community, particularly from schools. The Nature Conservancy Council took a leading role in the campaign by designing wall-charts and audio-visual displays, encouraging local initiatives and commissioning W G Teagle's well-known study of West Midland urban wildlife, *The Endless Village*. The present book is an independant product of the same genre. There are encouraging signs that, in some quarters at least, these initiatives are striking a vital spark. Soon may it burgeon into flame.

What I personally find rather disheartening about the future of Aberdeen's wildlife and indeed that of the whole of Britain, is that, whatever happens, an intangible but precious thing is being lost: the accidental. When, a hundred and thirty years ago, George Dickie stumbled across some pools near Stocket road containing the beautiful alga, *Volvox globator*, he had the joy of a completely unexpected discovery: it became, in that sense, *his* 'locality'. That sort of experience will be difficult to find in the Aberdeen of the future, when every square inch of land will be planned, graded, scheduled, and given an appropriate label. Today, Dickie would not find *Volvox* by accident: he would travel by car to the nature reserve, park his car by the refreshment kiosk and join the queue over the duckboarding to where the warden is 'interpreting' the site to a throng of squealing schoolchildren. Collecting would, of course, be forbidden.

The natural history of Aberdeen's future will depend, as it always has, on man's treatment of his surroundings. If he uses them as a beast of burden to kick and beat into submission he will himself be the loser; by exercising care, constraint and compassion, he will win a steady and harmonious yield. Whatever happens, man will be pulling the strings. In the brave new world which gapes in front of us, let us hope that the newt in the pond and the iris in the hedgebank will continue to find sympathisers in the human world, just as a timid field mouse, two centuries ago, found a champion in Rabbie Burns:

> I'm truly sorry Man's dominion
> Has broken Nature's social union
> An' justifies th'ill opinion
> Which makes thee startle
> At me, thy poor, earth-born companion
> An' fellow-mortal.

Breeding Birds of Aberdeen City
(including the urban and suburban land and Hazlehead Park; excluding the rocky shore and open country)

Confirmed breeding

Great Crested Grebe	Willow Warbler
Heron	Goldcrest
Mallard	Spotted Flycatcher
Tufted Duck	Dunnock
Eider	Meadow Pipit
Mute Swan	Pied Wagtail
Sparrowhawk	Grey Wagtail
Kestrel	Starling
Capercaillie	Greenfinch
Partridge	Goldfinch
Pheasant	Linnet
Moorhen	Redpoll
Coot	Bullfinch
Oystercatcher	Chaffinch
Lapwing	Corn Bunting
Snipe	Yellowhammer
Woodcock	Reed Bunting
Curlew	House Sparrow
Common Sandpiper	Tree Sparrow
Redshank	75 species
Greater Black-backed Gull	
Herring Gull	**Probable breeding**
Common Gull	
Stock Dove	Teal
Feral Pigeon	Red Grouse
Wood Pigeon	Red-legged Partridge
Collared Dove	Water Rail
Barn Owl	Short-eared Owl
Tawny Owl	Hawfinch
Long-eared Owl	6 species
Swift	
Great Spotted Woodpecker	**Possible breeding**
Skylark	
Swallow	Little Grebe
House Martin	Goosander
Sand Martin	Merlin
Carrion Crow	Ringed Plover
Rook	Black-headed Gull
Jackdaw	Common Tern
Magpie	Arctic Tern
Great Tit	Cuckoo
Blue Tit	Green Woodpecker
Coal Tit	Wheatear
Long-tailed Tit	Black Redstart
Treecreeper	Garden Warbler
Wren	Chiffchaff
Dipper	Siskin
Mistle Thrush	14 species
Song Thrush	
Blackbird	**No longer breeding**
Stonechat	
Robin	Little Tern
Sedge Warbler	Black Grouse
Blackcap	Corncrake
Whitethroat	Twite
Lesser Whitethroat	4 species

Bibliography

Aberdeen Floras

David Skene (c 1765-70)   manuscript, University of Aberdeen
Alexander Murray (1836)   Northern Flora (only first part published).
George Dickie (1836)   Flora Abredonensis.
'Surgeon Cow' (1836)   unpublished Flora of Aberdeen.
Paul Howard MacGillivray (1855)   Flowering plants and ferns growing in the neighbourhood of Aberdeen.
William MacGillivray (1855)   The Natural History of Deeside and Braemar.
George Dickie (1860)   The Botanist's Guide to the Counties of Aberdeen, Banff and Kincardine.
James William Helenus Trail (1923)   The Flora of the City Parish of Aberdeen

Aberdeen Faunas

William MacGillivray (1843)   A History of the Molluscous Animals of the Counties of Aberdeen, Kincardine and Banff.
George Sim (1903)   The Vertebrate Fauna of 'Dee'.

Historical Descriptions of the City of Aberdeen

John Spalding   Memorialls of the Trubles in Scotland and England 1624-1645. Spalding Club, 1850.
Gordon of Rothiemay (1661)   Aberdoniae Utriusque Descriptio. Spalding Club, 1842.
J Adair (1703)   The coast of Scotland from the Red Head to Aberdeen.
Francis Douglas (1782 repr.1827)   A general description of the coast of Scotland from Edinburgh to Cullen.
Murdo Downie (1792)   Marine Survey, east coast of Scotland.
The Statistical Account of Scotland (1782-94)
William Duncan (1837)   Description of the coast between Aberdeen and Leith.
New Statistical Account of Scotland (1843)

Modern Works concerning the City of Aberdeen

Cruikshank J (1934)   Dyce - Its history and traditions. Wyllie.
Fraser G M (1904)   Historical Aberdeen. The Green and its Story. Smith, Aberdeen. reprinted Robin Callander, 1980.
Fraser G M (1921)   The Old Deeside Road. Aberdeen Univ. Press, reprinted Robin Callander, 1980.
Graham Cuthbert (1972)   Portrait of Aberdeen and Deeside. Hale, London.

Hamilton, Henry (ed. 1960)　　　Third Statistical Account of Scotland: The County of Aberdeen. Collins.

Keith, Alexander (1972)　　　A Thousand Years of Aberdeen. Aberdeen Univ. Press.

McKenzie, Hugh (1953)　　　Third Statistical Account of Scotland: The City of Aberdeen. Oliver & Boyd.

Millman R N (1975)　　　The Making of the Scottish Landscape. Batsford, London.

Robbie, William (1873)　　　Aberdeen -Its traditions and history. Wyllie.

Walton K, Mellor R and
Hamilton P (1963)　　　Aberdeen. Scot. Geog. Mag, *79*, 69.

Wyness, Fenton (1963)　　　City by the Grey North Sea. Reid & Son, Aberdeen.

Natural History References

Aberdeen Archaeological Unit (1978)　　　Aberdeen: the town beneath the city. Aberdeen Museums and Art Gallery.

Bourne W R P (1978)　　　Herring Gulls nesting on buildings in eastern Scotland. NE Scotland Bird Report, 45-46.

Bourne W R P (1979)　　　Prolonged parental care in Herring Gulls nesting in towns in eastern Scotland. Bird Study, *26*, 196-197.

Bremner Alexander (1921)　　　The Physical Geology of the Dee and Don Valleys. Aberdeen Univ. Press.

British Association for the Advancement
Of Science(1935)　　　A scientific survey of Aberdeen and District, 1-123.

Burnett J H (1964)　　　Vegetation of Scotland

Carnegie H M (1975)　　　Ecology of dicotyledonous weeds of arable land in north east Scotland. unpublished PhD thesis, University of Aberdeen.

City of Aberdeen, Dept. of Leisure and
Recreation.　　　Guides to Hazlehead, Loirston and Brimmond Country Parks; Woodside, the Old Deeside Line Walk and Aberdeen's urban parks.

Cowie W (1903)　　　Macro-lepidoptera of Aberdeen and neighbour-hood. Trans. Aberdeen NHSS, 20-35.

Davidson M B and Young M R (1980)　　　A seasonal invertebrate survey of the River Dee (Aberdeenshire) and its main tributaries. unpublished report for NCC.

Dickie G (1838)　　　Remarks on mosses found in the neighbourhood of Aberdeen. Mag of Zool. and Bot. *2*, 412-419.

Durno S E (1957)　　　Certain aspects of vegetational history in north east Scotland. Scot. Geog. Mag. *73*, 176-184.

Forest A (1950)　　　The terrestrial mollusca of Aberdeenshire and Kincardineshire. Scot. Nat. *62*, 53.

Forman, Bruce (1951)　　　The spiders of Aberdeenshire. Scot. Nat. *63*, 137-155.

ibid　　　(1951)　　　The harvestmen of Aberdeenshire. Scot. Nat. *63*, 156-158.

Gerrie B M (1979)　　　The Potamogetons of north east Scotland. unpublished MSc thesis, University of Aberdeen.

Gibbons E (1972)　　　Vegetation survey of part of the Deeside railway line. unpublished MSc thesis, University of Aberdeen.

Glentworth R and Muir J W (1963) — The soils of the Country around Aberdeen, Inverurie and Fraserburgh. HMSO, Edinburgh.

Grampian Regional Council (1977) — Ecological survey of the river Don to river Ythan. GRC report.

Hall G H (1927) — Sea trout from the tidal waters of the Don and the Ythan. Fishery Board for Scot. Salmon Fisheries, Edinburgh.

Kerr L G (1977) — A study of the macrophyte flora of Corby, Lily and Bishop's Lochs. unpublished MSc thesis, University of Aberdeen.

Knox Alan (ed. 1974-79) — North East Scotland Bird Reports.

MacGillivray W (1843) — Description of Vespertilio Daubentonii from specimens found in Aberdeenshire. Edinburgh New Philosophical Journal,*31*, 255-259.

MacGillivay W (1901) — 'A Memorial Tribute to William MacGillivray. Edinburgh.

ibid (1910) — Life of William MacGillivray, Ornithologist, Professor of Natural History at Aberdeen University. Murray, London.

Mearns J (1903) — Hymenoptera around Aberdeen. Trans. Aberdeen NHSS, *1* 36-38.

ibid (1905) — Diptera found around Aberdeen, *3*, 117-123.
ibid (1905) — Coleoptera around Aberdeen,*3*, 124-126.
ibid (1905) — Hemiptera-Heteroptera, Orthoptera and Odonata around Aberdeen, *4*, 170-171.

Milne A (1941) — Some ecological aspects of the intertidal area of the estuary of the Aberdeenshire Dee. Trans. Roy. Soc. Edin. *60*, 1.

Palmer R M (1974 et seq) — Lepidoptera of Aberdeenshire and Kincardine-shire. Ent. Rec. (1974) 33-44, 273-284; (1975) 180-188, 218-224; (1976) 121-126, 196-203, 286-293; (with M R Young 1977) 239-243.

Reid W (1893) — List of Lepidoptera of Aberdeenshire and Kincardineshire. Br. Nat. reprint, vols 1-3, 1891-93 and completed.

Ritchie James (1922) — Mammals of Deeside. Deeside Field, 46

Ritchie J C (1952) — Ecological survey of heath vegetation in the neighbourhood of Aberdeen. unpublished MSc thesis, University of Aberdeen.

Ritchie W and Buchan G M (1978) — Historical and recent changes in Aberdeen beach and Donmouth. Aberdeen Univ. Review.

Ritchie W, Rose N and Smith J S (1978) — Beaches of North East Scotland. Dept. of Geography, University of Aberdeen.

Scottish Development Agency and Aberdeen District Council (1981) — Tullos Hill, Aberdeen. Recommendations for reinstatement and management. Derek Lovejoy & Partners.

Shalwindi F (1977) — Flora, soil and soil fauna of grazed and ungrazed grassland on Brimmond Hill. unpublished MSc thesis, University of Aberdeen.

Sim John (1878) — The Botany of Scotston Moor. Nat. Hist. Soc. Aberdeen.

Simpson J (1903) — Catalogue of Echinoderms found at Aberdeen and. Trans. Aberdeen NHSS, 39-43.

ibid (1904) — Marine Conchology of 'Dee'. Trans. Aberdeen NHSS, 64-86.

Skene, MacGregor (1925)   American plants on Deeside. Deeside Field Club Mag, 23.

Smith W (1903)   The dangers of Aberdeen Bay and proposed precautions. Trans. Aberdeen Philosoph. Soc. 2, 120.

Swann R   Blackbird and Robin roosts in Aberdeen. Bird Study, 22, 93-98.

Thomas P (1980)   A survey of semi-natural areas in the City of Aberdeen District. unpublished report for NCC.

Trail J W H (1899)   Florula of a piece of waste ground at Aberdeen. Ann. Scot. Nat. Hist., 5, 231-245.

ibid   (1911)   Man's influence on the indigenous flora of Aberdeen. Ann. Scot. Nat. Hist., 175-180, 232-240.

ibid   (1878)   On the progress of zoology in Aberdeen and its neighbourhood. Trans. Nat. Hist. Soc. Aberdeen, 7-23.

ibid   (1878)   Lists of Lepidoptera and other insects of 'Dee', Trans. Nat. Hist. Soc. Aberdeen, 28-47; Lists of Araneidae (spiders) of 'Dee' 45-54; Galls and their makers in 'Dee', 55-83.

Walker, Alexander (1893)   The Commonty of Perwinnes. Aberdeen Journals.

Watt A S (1931)   Preliminary observations on Scottish beechwoods. J. Ecol., 19, 137-157; 321-359.

Wynne-Edwards V C (1952)   The centenary of William MacGillivray. Scot. Nat., 64, 65-69.

References to the natural history of Aberdeen can be traced in the following journals: Annals of Scottish Natural History, The Deeside Field (1922-37; 1953-70), Scottish Birds, The Scottish Naturalist, Transactions of the Botanical Society of Edinburgh, Transactions of Aberdeen Working Mens' Natural History and Scientific Society.

Recommended General Reading

Allen David Elliston (1976)   The Naturalist in Britain. A Social History. Allen Lane, London.

Anderson M L (1967)   History of Forestry in Scotland. Nelson, London.

Chinery Michael (1977)   The Natural History of the Garden. Collins, London.

Gilbert John M (1979)   Hunting and Hunting Reserves in Medieval Scotland. John Donald, Edinburgh.

Mabey Richard (1973)   The Unofficial Countryside. Collins, London.

Murton R K (1971)   Man and Birds. Collins, London.

Owen Denis (1978)   Towns and Gardens. The natural history of Britain and northern Europe. Hodder & Stoughton.

Teagle W G (1978)   The Endless Village. NCC, Shrewbury.

INDEXES
OF WILDLIFE, PERSONS AND PLACES

WILD ANIMALS AND PLANTS

I have used English names, where they exist, of animals and plants in the main body of the text, and these are listed alphabetically in this index, together with their scientific names. The scientific names of higher plants follow those of Clapham, Tutin and Warburg (second edition, 1964) except in a few instances where these have been superseded. For those of birds I was guided by the British Trust for Ornithology Guide (1971) and similar recognised authorities have been followed for the other groups.

PERSONS

PLACES